'Helen Morgan in *The Work of Whiteness* brilliant
privilege within social and psychoanalytical con
she reaches across the Atlantic to include the c
American authors such as Robin DiAngelo who
to the essential, necessary engagement of whites in a collective self-reflective
motion. This motion allows author Morgan as well as other whites in the field of
psychoanalysis to adhere to the long-overdue necessity of admitting social and
political influences into the psychological realm. This white inward gaze also
relieves Africanist individuals of remaining the *problem of racism* of which Du
Bois spoke. Morgan's book adds much to our sparse collection of those white
authors within the field of psychoanalysis who endeavour to bring hope to the
challenges of racism. We welcome her unique, rich, powerful voice that calls for
us to be awake to the increasing global demands for racial equity.'

Fanny Brewster, *Ph.D., M.F.A., LP, Author of* The Racial Complex: A
Jungian Perspective on Culture and Race

'Helen Morgan has written a challenging, compassionate, thoughtful, erudite
and profoundly incisive book which directs our gaze to the largely hidden and
uncomfortable phenomenon of whiteness. Her thinking crosses boundaries and
disciplines in a fluid but always coherent way. This is not just a book about
psychoanalysis and racism, but engages us all to reflect on deep and often
damaging assumptions and preconceptions shaping and driving our personal,
clinical and social lives. Her work is the culmination of many years of therapeutic,
organisational and leadership experience, from which she extrapolates and
translates so that we can all learn. In this area there are only a few genuinely
probing and creatively disruptive texts, but this is another and I encourage our
institutions, trainings and clinical communities to promote and disseminate it.'

Andrew Cooper, *Professor of Social Work at the Tavistock
Centre and University of East London, Adult Psychoanalytic
Psychotherapist, Author of* Conjunctions: Social Work,
Psychoanalysis and Society

'*The Work of Whiteness* is a major addition to the psychoanalytic literature on
race, racism and colonialism. Writing from personal and professional experience
as a leading Jungian analyst, and fully acknowledging the tarnished history of her
profession, Helen Morgan shows how we might understand white privilege and
the defences around "white fragility" that perpetuate racism even in apparently
liberal contexts. This is a vital book for all of us who want to better understand
how whiteness does its work.'

Stephen Frosh, *Professor in the Department of Psychosocial Studies,
Birkbeck, University of London, Author of* Those Who Come After:
Postmemory, Acknowledgement and Forgiveness

'This book is a gift to all of us, because whiteness is an under-examined notion that distorts humanity. European colonisation of the Americas, Africa, India, the Middle East, Australia among other parts of the world, has led to an entrenched and unconscious assumption that white is superior. With a psychoanalytic lens, Helen Morgan's book goes beneath the surface of whiteness to explore its nature and provide truths that should be faced by all of us, especially those who work in the helping professions.'

Frank Lowe, *Consultant Social Worker and Psychoanalytic Psychotherapist, Tavistock Clinic, Editor of* Thinking Space: Promoting Thinking About Race, Culture, and Diversity in Psychotherapy and Beyond

The Work of Whiteness

'Whiteness' is a politically constructed category which needs to be understood and dismantled because the system of racism so embedded within our society harms us all. It has profound implications for human psychology, an understanding of which is essential for supporting the movement for change. This book explores these implications from a psychoanalytic and Jungian analytic perspective.

The 'fragility' of whiteness, the colour-blind approach and the silencing process of disavowal as they develop in the childhood of white liberal families are considered as means of maintaining white privilege and racism. A critique of the colonial roots of psychoanalytic theories of Freud and Jung leads to questioning the de-linking of the individual from society in modern day analytic thinking. The concept of the cultural complex is suggested as a useful means of connecting the individual and the social. Examples from the author's clinical practice as well as from public life are used to illustrate the argument.

Relatively few black people join the psychoanalytic profession and those who do describe training and membership as a difficult and painful process. How racism operates in clinical work, supervision and our institutions is explored, and whilst it can seem an intractable problem, proposals are given for ways forward. This book will be of great importance to psychoanalysts, psychotherapists, social workers and all those with an interest in the role of white privilege on mental health.

Helen Morgan is a Jungian analytic training analyst and supervisor, and Fellow of the British Psychotherapy Foundation. Her background is in therapeutic communities with adolescents and in adult mental health. She was Chair of the British Association of Psychotherapists between 2003 and 2007, and Chair of the British Psychoanalytic Council between 2015 and 2018. She has published a number of papers, including several on racism.

The Work of Whiteness

A Psychoanalytic Perspective

Helen Morgan

Routledge
Taylor & Francis Group

LONDON AND NEW YORK

First published 2021
by Routledge
2 Park Square, Milton Park, Abingdon, Oxon OX14 4RN

and by Routledge
605 Third Avenue, New York, NY 10158

Routledge is an imprint of the Taylor & Francis Group, an informa business

British Library Cataloguing-in-Publication Data
A catalogue record for this book is available from the British Library

Library of Congress Cataloging-in-Publication Data
A catalog record for this book has been requested

ISBN: 978-0-367-21835-5 (hbk)
ISBN: 978-0-367-21836-2 (pbk)
ISBN: 978-0-429-26644-7 (ebk)

Typeset in Times New Roman
by Apex CoVantage, LLC

Contents

The book cover   viii
Preface   ix
Acknowledgements   xiv

Introduction   1

1   Whiteness   12

2   The legacy of slavery   25

3   Race and racism   43

4   The disavowal of whiteness   57

5   Freud and Jung   72

6   The racial complex   85

7   Racism and the psychoanalytic profession   101

8   Race and supervision   118

    Epilogue: the work of whiteness   130

Bibliography   137
Index   143

The book cover

As he was walking to his London studio one day in the 1960s, the Guyanese artist Frank Bowling came across a large white swan trapped in a pool of oil from which it was battling to fly free. Struck by the ferocious determination of the bird, Bowling painted sufficient versions of the image to fill the first room of the retrospective of his work at Tate Britain. The painting on the cover of this book is one of them. As I stood before the canvas in the summer of 2019, I was struck by this image of whiteness caught as it was by the consequences of exploitation. It seemed to me that Bowling had captured something essential of the force and energy with which the white bird struggled against the inevitability of its fate.

Preface

I am often asked why, as a white woman, I concern myself with the problem of racism. I imagine this is a question rarely put to black colleagues who write and speak on the subject. It will be assumed that it is an aspect of their lived experience and they have no choice but to be conscious of the reality of racism, both in its overt extreme forms and in the subtler microaggressions of daily life within a racist system. I am considered, and have learnt to consider myself, to be 'white', a person of no colour, an inherited identity which includes the option of invisibility and ignorance regarding racism except as an abstract phenomenon that exists elsewhere, regrettable but not really my problem. This light-hued skin I have inherited comes with a blindfold, a free ticket, a permit to disregard the matter altogether. 'Whiteness', like other categories that dominate aspects of the social hierarchies, gets to say what is the norm and can therefore avoid interrogation.

I was born and brought up in Bristol, a city in the west of England, about 120 miles from London. Bristol is a wealthy metropolis which, along with Liverpool, Glasgow and London, was one of the most important ports in the British transatlantic slave trade and prospered greatly from the profits of that trade. The wealthier of those traders were memorialised through street names, schools, theatres, pubs and statues throughout the city.

The seventeenth-century merchant and Member of Parliament Edward Colston was particularly honoured for his philanthropy in the city. I recall efforts made to recognise his part in the trading of enslaved Africans when I was at school in the 1960s – all of which were blocked. It was only during the Black Lives Matter protests in the summer of 2020 that some of Bristol's residents took the matter into their own hands and pulled down his statue in the centre of the city and sunk it in the same harbour from which his ships set sail on their terrible mission. This has led to a long overdue public examination of Bristol's past and its present-day relation to such monuments.

As a response to post-war labour shortages in the UK, residents of the British colonies were invited to come to the country to work and many arrived between 1948 and 1971 from the Caribbean. These people are known as 'the Windrush generation' in reference to the ship MV Empire Windrush, which arrived in the UK in 1948, bringing workers from islands of the Caribbean. Along with the unfamiliar cold and wet of Britain, they had to cope with hostility and racism from much of the white British population who were unused to living alongside black people in such numbers. Many of the new arrivals came to live in Bristol, mainly confined to the inner-city area of St Pauls. As was the case throughout the country, signs went up in shops and boarding houses declaring: 'No dogs, No blacks, No Irish'.

Such signs are illegal now, but the racism remains. In 2017 the 'Windrush scandal' began to break in the British newspapers after it emerged that hundreds of Commonwealth citizens, many of whom were from the Windrush generation, had been wrongly detained, deported and denied human rights under the 'Hostile Environment' immigration policy of the Conservative Government. Despite a Review into what took place that was published in March 2020, there has been no apology and only a few have received compensation. Furthermore, at the time of writing, the policy is still in place.

Living in a middle class suburb of the city and attending a Catholic grammar school which was almost entirely white, I rarely came across black people in any significant way. If asked to define who I was, I would not have even considered including whiteness as an element of my identity. As I understood it, I and my family, friends and fellow schoolmates were just the norm. Taught in part by nuns, we learnt of the work of the missionaries in Africa, India and South America and collected charitable pennies for the 'poor' African babies. Africans were to be patronised, or – warned by adults about certain parts of town – black people living here were to be feared.

Despite the changes brought about by the Civil Rights Movements in the 1960s and 70s, despite the upsurge of black culture bringing the soundtrack of Tamla Motown and Reggae to my adolescent and university years, it is curious how blind I remained to my whiteness and my racism. Looking back, it has been living through particular moments in my personal history that shocked me into re-examining my whiteness and hence my place in a world organised along racial lines.

In the early 70s I left university and, for family reasons, returned to Bristol and worked as a teacher in a large secondary school in a white working class estate on a neglected edge of the city. Children were bussed in from St Pauls, so that roughly two thirds were white and a third were black. Growing up in a middle class suburb of the city, both St Pauls and the school area were unknown to me and I found myself having to manage complex and entirely unfamiliar tensions and conflicts between these different groups of school children. Suddenly I was confronted with a whole set of cultures and assumptions of which I had previously only a vague awareness, and I was struck by just how sheltered and ignorant I was.

A few years later, travelling south and east through Asia with friends, assumptions we had no idea were so embedded within us were constantly challenged. Stopping a while in cultures that were so very different from our own gradually shifted any implicitly held notion that ours was the 'norm'. As the distance from home grew, so did our realisation that the religious, cultural, political and intersubjective ways of being that we took for granted were just that: one way of being among many, many others.

One example is a small incident that occurred in Hong Kong on our way to Japan. At the time it was possible to visit China, although only as part of strictly policed and guided tours and, whilst waiting for permits, we went to the cinema. It was a Chinese film and the subject was the opium wars of the mid-nineteenth century. Back at home I had seen the odd B movie based on these and I was used to the narrative of handsome, heroic British soldiers fighting for what was right and just against the cruel barbarians. The Chinese were depicted in British popular historical film and literature as brutal, 'inscrutable' and therefore dangerous, dishonourable and untrustworthy. Sitting in the heat of the Hong Kong cinema, a very different perspective was on view. Here the Chinese soldiers were handsome and brave whilst the British were fat, ugly and capable of terrible barbaric deeds. It was, we were realising, a matter of who gets to tell the story that determines our perception of the world.

Having returned to the UK, I worked in therapeutic communities – first with adolescent boys in the west country and later with adults with mental health difficulties in London which gave me my first real experience of working with and alongside black clients and colleagues. At a staff meeting I referred to one of the residents as 'half-caste'. At the end a black colleague took me to one side and patiently spoke with me about the term, its history, its implications and what it meant for a white person to use this about someone. It shouldn't be down to the black individual to educate the white, but I am very grateful to this friend that he did so with me. Without making me feel bad, his generosity helped me to understand just how much words matter and how important it is that white people listen to and think through what words might do damage to those who are black.

At the same time, I was training to become a Jungian analyst. Very early on I came across some of Jung's writing on women and my feminist soul rebelled. I could not accept his pronouncements on the 'feminine', the 'anima' and, even more so, the 'animus'. I had to decide how much I would put aside such objections in order that I could continue with the training. I know well the 'man of his time' argument – I have used it on myself many times. It's a perspective with some validity but I learnt that there is a price to pay internally when one is required to swallow the indigestible as a part of the greater meal.

But it was a few years later when I read Farhad Dalal's 1988 paper 'Jung: A Racist' that I came to re-examine some of Jung's writings on the so-called 'primitive' as well as some key aspects of Jungian theory. I was stunned by the realisation that I must have read the passages Dalal quoted several times during my training but either had failed to even register them or had dismissed them as just old fashioned without further thought. Trainees and our teachers were all white as were all our training patients. In theoretical seminars no one raised questions about the deeper racist implications of some of the material we were discussing. In clinical seminars, were a black person to appear in a white patient's dream, it was taken for granted that they were a representation of the Shadow. No one thought to question what a white figure appearing in a black person's dream might mean.

At the time when I was training in my 30s, the racist epithets and jokes, the golliwogs and the Black and White Minstrel Show were on their way out – at least from the liberal circles I frequented. I abhorred acts of blatant racism, went on marches to protest against South African apartheid and discrimination of all kinds and read widely. I had a few black friends and was struggling with the complexities of a mixed relationship. The fact that, nevertheless, I had still been blind to the racist assumptions deep within some of the texts I had read was disturbing. It was if there was a blank space in me, a blindness and a dumbness which was supported by the world in which I lived. I turned to black writers who were articulating something I could not see. Slowly, from out of the white canvas painted by the world I was born into and inhabited, emerged my own white silhouette and a glimmer of its shadow. I was beginning to see aspects of my racism and wondered that it had never arisen in my intensive training analysis. Evidently something important was being denied or disavowed.

Like an internal set of the three monkeys, deafness, blindness and silence have been the main features of my relationship to my whiteness and its meaning. A series of lesser and greater experiences have occurred throughout my life which have jolted me into a shift in awareness about the racialised world and my place in it and which, in turn, have provoked a curiosity to find out more. I see this silence and colour blindness reflected in most of my white world, together with a common discomfort and dis-ease whenever the matter is raised. This intrigues me. What is going on within the white psyche that produces such anxiety and results in silence? Why do we have so little stamina for grappling with this powerful and pervasive dynamic? Exploration of such questions have led me to formulate thinking about how disavowal in regard to racism operates within the white psyche, and the dead, silent place that is created between the two dividing screens that form the vertical split of the defence.

As I came to the end of writing this book on May 25, 2020, the African American George Floyd was killed during an arrest in Minneapolis, Minnesota, by a policeman kneeling on his neck for almost nine minutes whilst fellow officers looked on. This, following on from the shooting of Breonna Taylor by Louisville police in March 2020, led to a surge of outrage and protests all around the globe and a reactivation of the Black Lives Matter (BLM) movement which had come together when George Zimmerman was acquitted of murder after shooting Trayvon Martin dead in 2012 as he walked back from a corner shop in Florida.

These protests came as we and the rest of the world were reeling from the impact of Covid-19. It became apparent early on that this hit the Black, Asian and Minority Ethnic (BAME) community disproportionately hard. In June 2020, a public Health England report contained alarming statistics and found that the unequal impact may be explained by social and economic inequalities, racism, discrimination and stigma, differing risks at work and inequalities in the prevalence of conditions such as obesity, diabetes, hypertension and asthma, all factors increasing vulnerability to and the severity of Covid-19.

This book comes from a conviction that racism and white privilege and supremacy not only does untold harm to the black 'Other' but also damages white people. I do not in any way equate the injuries, but leaving the appeal to white people to voluntarily address their racism and privilege from altruism alone will not get us far. We have to see and feel the abomination this system is, which hurts us all.

The model of 'individuation' as a way of describing the creative development of the psyche is an important concept within Jungian theory. It is one of the terms that Dalal challenges but, whilst it needs re-examination and re-visioning, it remains for me a valid and useful term. Very different from 'individualism', individuation is defined by Andrew Samuels (1985) as 'a movement towards wholeness by means of an integration of conscious and unconscious parts of the personality. This involves personal and emotional conflict resulting in differentiation from general conscious attitudes and from the collective unconscious' (p. 102).

In her book on African Americans and Jungian psychology, Fanny Brewster (2017) points out: 'Jung says that Africanist people are, for the most part, unable to individuate. He says that we do not have the level of consciousness necessary for such a feat' (p. 43). It is hard to see how a black individual encounters such a notion and manages to keep on reading, but I also wonder who is it, black or white, whose path of individuation is impeded through a lack of the necessary level of consciousness?

When white people choose to stay blind, deaf and silent concerning our own privilege and its impact on the black 'Other', we are opting to remain unconscious of a crucial aspect of our lives and of ourselves. This part of our shadow has been whitewashed out of view, but then what colours, what potential, what depth might we be missing? And who is it then who do not have 'the level of consciousness necessary' for the feat of individuation?

This then is my answer to queries regarding my motivation for concern with this matter. It is neither altruistic nor, I believe, neurotic, but comes from a need to investigate a part mostly hidden from myself. Its invisibility is supported and conspired with by a global system of power relations which brings much material privilege and freedom from discrimination, but it does me harm and acts as a block to my own path of individuation.

References

Brewster, F. (2017) *African Americans and Jungian Psychology: Leaving the Shadows*. London: Routledge.

Dalal, F. (1988) Jung: A Racist. *British Journal of Psychotherapy*, 4(3), 263–279.

Samuels, A. (1985) *Jung and the Post-Jungians*. London, Boston, and Henley: Routledge & Kegan Paul.

Acknowledgements

Over the years I have been fortunate to be involved in some powerful conversations around the subjects of racism and whiteness with friends, colleagues and patients. These discussions, whilst not always comfortable, have challenged and shaken up my thinking and allowed me to build up some resilience. Presenting papers and teaching on the subject gave me the space to develop my thinking through engagement with others from whom I have learnt much. Throughout the writing of the book I am fortunate to have been supported and encouraged by good friends and I thank them all. In particular, I wish to mention a dear friend, Sheila Simpson, whom I met at university and who has been travelling with me – both literally and metaphorically – since that time. She has read and edited every part of the book, discussed the ideas and theory with me and generally kept me going. Many thanks to her.

Introduction

The two central terms in the title of this book, 'whiteness' and 'psychoanalytic', are fraught with complexity as each carries uncertainty and even conflict as to their application. Whilst acknowledging the limitations and confusions of the words, choices have to be made regarding the terminology to be used throughout a book such as this. The best I can do is lay out the quandaries and objections as far as I understand them and then ask the reader to bear with them whilst holding the questions in mind.

Dilemmas and paradoxes

The subjects of 'race', 'racism', 'whiteness', 'blackness' and 'colour' are riddled with paradox and dilemmas. The belief that humans can be divided into biologically distinct and essentially different groups has been widely discredited by the evidence from the Human Genome Project which explains that any visible differences in skin colour and features are a matter of relatively trivial aspects of history and geography. The divide was constructed in the service of global power relations and some argue that to even use the term 'race' is itself racist, as it serves to perpetuate a myth and a constructed division.

The point is a valid one, yet so is the reality that we have been split into different 'races' by those who have power and this division has substantial social, economic and political implications despite – maybe because of – its lack of biological substance. Racism and the supremacy of whiteness continues to be one of the most powerful and pervading determinates for the organisation of wealth and power throughout the world. In my view we need to stay with the concept even as we decry its effects if we are to face its implications for power relationships and the division of resources in twenty-first-century society.

The Civil Rights Movements of the 1960s took the term 'black' and asserted its beauty, challenging the derogatory implications of its usage within the white lexicon. As a *political* category it came to be used as an umbrella term for all those considered to be 'not white' and so suffer from the oppression and discrimination caused by the system of white supremacy and privilege. More recently there is debate within and between BAME communities as to whether the original reclaiming of 'black' as a positive attribute by the Civil Rights Movement has moved to a point where 'brown' or 'yellow' and other ethnic categories need distinction and reclamation. Besides recognising the reality and importance of the debate, this is not a matter for a white author in a book that is focused on the 'white' experience. From this perspective, whilst white racism is constellated somewhat differently in relation to the various groups who are deemed to exist outside of whiteness, the *basic* dynamics that operate within the white psyche are more or less the same.

Where the dividing line is placed, who gets to be perceived as white and to sit at the centre of this particular arrangement of power and privilege and who must reside at the margins, is not a fixed matter but shifts according to both history and geography. At different moments in history Jews, the Irish, Latinos and Southern Europeans have all been regarded as 'black' – or at least 'non-white'. At other times and other places, they are accepted as 'white'. How this is decided seems to be an emergent process depending on the political and economic forces in operation and what best serves the profit motive of the capitalist system at that time and location.

My brief biography described in the Preface is a personal one unique to me, and every other white person reading this will have had very different histories depending on age, ancestry, gender, ethnicity, geography, class, etc. The more overt racist activities and symbols of the 50s and 60s are no longer acceptable and it is often argued that later generations are freer of these racist attitudes. However, the evidence of the research implies something more complicated, and it may be that it is just buried deeper into the psyche. As Terrance MacMullan (2009) puts it:

> I worry that we might well get people to stop using race talk without affecting in the slightest the more subtle and habituated features of racism that still adversely affect the lives of millions of people and deny us the fruits of true community'.
>
> (p. 2)

White supremacy and white privilege

Distinguishing between 'white supremacy' and 'white privilege', Shannon Sullivan (2006) notes the shift in the twentieth century from *de jure* to *de facto* racism. When slavery as an institution was abolished in the US in 1865 it was replaced by state and local statutes which became known as the Jim Crow laws (after a black minstrel show character). These laws, which stayed on the statute book for more than a hundred years, were intended to marginalise African Americans by denying them the right to vote, hold jobs, get an education or other life chances. Those who attempted to defy these laws often faced arrest, fines, jail sentences, violence and death.

Laws which *actively* enforced segregation and discrimination did not exist as such in the UK, but discrimination was overt, common and legal until the Race

Relations Act was passed in 1968, making it illegal to refuse housing, employment or public services to a person on the grounds of colour, race, ethnic or national origins in Great Britain.

However, as Sullivan (2006) points out, the ending of the Jim Crow laws in the US and making discrimination illegal in European countries did *not* mean the end of white domination,

> but a significant shift in its predominant mode of operation. It was no longer socially acceptable in most white circles and institutions to openly proclaim racist beliefs. The 'good' (= nonracist) white person was supposed to treat everyone equally, which was taken to mean not noticing a person's race at all. In this atmosphere of alleged colourblindness, racism continued and continues to function without the use of race related terms.
>
> (p. 5)

Sullivan (p. 5) distinguishes 'white supremacy' where 'white domination is consciously embraced and affirmed' from 'white privilege' which 'goes to great lengths not to be heard'. 'White supremacists' are members and groups who engage in overt racist acts and assert that their whiteness means superiority. They seek an all-white nation or, at least, one where 'non-whites' are subservient. Whilst these groups are worryingly growing in numbers throughout Europe and the US, they are not the main focus of this book.

This distinction is pragmatically useful but, again, creates yet another binary which can mislead us. The existence of those who publicly avow white supremacy and engage in overtly racist language and acts can allow 'white liberals' to perpetuate the illusion that, being not like them, we are therefore not racist. Meanwhile our racism, which has the same roots as that of the white supremacist, goes underground to operate at the more invisible level of white privilege and white solipsism. Racism conveniently comes to be seen as an act or a word rather than a primary system which constructs our world and from which we benefit. The very existence of avowed white supremacist groups provides a receptacle for the projection of the racism of the white liberal who then can retreat into indignation, disgust and disavowal.

Nevertheless, with these caveats in mind, I maintain the distinction for the purposes of my argument which concerns the unconscious dynamics that support and keep hidden the racism of white liberals, in particular the defence of disavowal. Such a defence does not operate in the white supremacist, whose actions and beliefs are driven by other unconscious dynamics. 'White liberal' suggests an irony which pokes at our libertarian, progressive, right-on stance, implying something darker might be driving us and of which we need reminding. But it also acknowledges the liberal commitment to justice and fairness, its dis-ease with its privileged position and the genuine wish for change. 'White supremacist' is a more brutal label within which it is hard to find anything but despair.

A 'psychoanalytic' perspective

The shift in the mode of operation of white domination from its overt expression to a more hidden, muted one suggests a psychoanalytic perspective might have a part to play in the understanding of how racism and white privilege is maintained individually and collectively. However, this proposal comes with many caveats.

I am using the term 'psychoanalytic' in its broadest sense to include the original Freudian view and all its various offspring – including Jungian analysis. The key assumption common to all approaches within this wide umbrella is that a large part of our psychological activity occurs outside of conscious awareness and control. Early life experiences are key in determining emotional development, social behaviour and interpersonal relationships throughout life. Internal defence mechanisms are formed to protect the individual from emotional pain and anxiety which, in themselves, may hinder later development and cause problems for the mental health of the individual. Such unconscious dynamics including these defence mechanisms occur in the individual but also in groups, organisations, societies and cultures. The differences *between* the various schools of thought within this overarching rubric is of little relevance to the subject of this book except for a few exceptions which I hope will be clear.

Over recent years psychoanalysts and Jungian analysts have developed an increasingly refined theoretical understanding of how racism operates in the individual psyche as well as the psychological impact on the person on the receiving end. The focus of our theories tends to be the way the racist thought or act is generated from within the psyche, how it may be part of a defensive process which includes splitting and projection and which contains the emotions of hate, fear and envy. These are helpful in analysing how the individual psyche utilises the racist structures and forms that underpin society, as well as giving insight into the impact such structures may have on the individual. However, the approach assumes a universality regarding the formulation of racist structures and removes the individual from socio-economic dynamics of power, privilege, domination and greed. Whilst helpful in deepening our understanding of the *effects* of racist power relations within the social world into which we are born on the individual psyche, there is the danger that they persuade us into thinking they are the *causes* of racism and the locus of its solution.

Racism is not just an act, word or event but a socio-economic-political process which forms a template of power relationships and hierarchies into which we in Western societies are born. The individual racist thought or act emerges from within that template. How we are affected by and respond to this hierarchy depends on where we are placed within that structure. The individual who is regarded as 'white' is born into the centre of that political arrangement with all the privilege that brings. Change in that system comes through political activism or shifts in economic factors or a mixture of both. It does not come from the couch.

Philip Cushman (2000) warns us to take care when theorising about the psychological dynamics of racism:

The racism that concerns us in the United States is not universal, ahistorical, or inevitable. It is the product of an intersection of local customs, power relations, and institutions that developed in Western Europe and then in the United States during the modern era (which began ca. 1600). Racism is the product of various political arrangements, and currently it serves many rather specific political purposes. It facilitates the exploitation of the 'Third World' and domestic labor and natural resources, the continuing destruction of the urban dispossessed, the manipulation of working-class labor and middle-class consumers, the control of voters, and the neutralization of resistance movements.

(p. 609)

By assuming an autonomous human separated from the social world, the focus of the psychoanalytic lens on the individual and the couple limits our understanding of suffering and trauma to the intra-psychic and the familial. With the exception of group analysis, we have de-coupled the person from their social world and from their social responsibility. The object relations school, in opposition to the 'instinctivists' of classical Freudian thought, place relationship as central in the development of the child. However, the focus is mainly limited to the connection with family members and little account is taken of the political order in which the family is located or the social context into which the baby arrives. In recent years 'relational' psychoanalysts have worked to include the two-way interaction between the individual and the socio-political context into which they are born.

Celia Brickman (2018) acknowledges that psychoanalysis is the study of the psyche not society, and that those theorists who have addressed the way that mechanisms of racism operate within the individual are doing necessary and important work. However, she argues that 'by discussing race and racism in terms of individual and interacting psyches, these accounts help obscure the wider and structural dimensions of racism'. She goes on to note that 'they have not yet taken into account the role of racism within the theoretical structure of psychoanalysis itself' and warns:

This fits only too comfortably with the (white) American predilection to think of racism as a personal outlook that an individual either does or does not have, or that does or does not occur within a particular setting or relationship.

(p. xv)

Racism created the races and is maintained for economic and political ends. However, whilst these wider social factors are rightly the concern of other disciplines, there is, I believe, an intermediate site of activity which involves an inter-weaving structure of complicity in order to maintain the status quo. The dynamics of white privilege, the fragility of whiteness and the processes of disavowal with its deadening silence come within the psychoanalytic remit – or at least there is overlap – and they need to be included in our analysis. For it is here where the intractable stubbornness of the system lies.

I argue, therefore, that a full comprehension of how racism operates in the white psyche and a strategy for radical effective transformation needs to include a psycho-analytic understanding of the unconscious psychological forces which are activated by a racist template and which work against change despite a conscious willing-ness to do so. Good intentions to shift white privilege will be ineffective unless we have some grasp of the forces that ensure its continuation. DiAngelo (2018) states: 'To increase the racial stamina that counters white fragility, we must reflect on the whole of our identities – and our racial group identity in particular. For white people, this means first struggling with what it means to be white' (p. 14).

Both Gordon (1993) and Dalal (2002) offer a comprehensive overview and critique of psychoanalytic explanations of racism. Dalal says:

> The overwhelming majority of the papers treated the topics of racism and prejudice as a symptom – as the external effect and social expression of inter-nal psychological dynamics. If and when the external social is given a role at all, it is secondary in that it is said to give a particular shape to the expression of these internal dynamics.
>
> (p. 77)

Dalal turns to the psychoanalyst and group analyst S.H. Foulkes, who posited the idea of the social unconscious and argued that, rather than looking to understand the social by seeking clues in the psychology of the individual,

> the clue to individual psychology is to be found in the psychology of the social and the group. Thus Foulkes' dictum is that it is in the understanding of social life that the foundation for the understanding of the individual per-sonality is to be found.
>
> (Dalal, 2002, p. 111)

Dalal connects this theory with Norbert Elias's concept of large social figura-tions or networks of independencies between people to explain the emergence and function of societal structures of power relationships.

Fakhry Davids, whose important book *Internal Racism* (2011) offers a sophis-ticated understanding of how racism works within the psyche and in interac-tion with the other from an object relations perspective, takes issue with Dalal's position:

> whilst Dalal's historicized account of how racism arises out of an imperative to distinguish 'haves' from 'must-not-haves' – and external world perspective – is compelling, he does little justice to the inner world dimension. Instead, he argues that a psychology of racism can give the impression that racism origi-nates from within, thereby obscuring the role of external, material forces in generating and maintaining it.
>
> (p. 9)

Davids sees this as problematic:

> Theoretical constructs are, of course, abstractions, but to use this to argue that little can be gained from understanding the role of the mind in perpetuating racism, in giving it an individual lease of life, is unconvincing. . . . Dalal and, to a lesser extent, Foulkes prioritize the social as the locus of motivation, but I think this extends the earlier polarized debate over origins and places a fully worked out psychology of racism beyond reach.
>
> (pp. 9–10)

I agree with Davids that an understanding of the role of the mind is essential if we are to fully comprehend how racism is perpetuated. However, it can only be part of the explanation. For the division of humanity into races for socio-political reasons preceded racism. The individual can and does adopt and act on the structure of racism provided in ways which fit with their particular psychological disposition, and the vicissitudes of how that is expressed in a specific patient is rightly the focus of analytic work. But the tenacity of racism despite analysis, training, organisational legislation and generally good intentions needs to include considerations of how white privilege is maintained through conscious and unconscious dynamics within the social order. The concepts of white fragility and the processes of disavowal are, in my view, important features of how that privilege is preserved and perpetuated and applying a psychoanalytic lens to these phenomena could be helpful.

The work of whiteness

Chapter 1 offers a brief history of the transatlantic slave trade from its beginnings in the fifteenth century to its ending in the nineteenth, with the focus on the development of the concept of the 'races' to justify the trade and colonialism. A psychoanalytic understanding of the transgenerational transmission of trauma is introduced. Black writers on this matter are referenced in consideration of the legacy of slavery for the descendants of its victims, but the main focus is on the impact of slavery on its perpetrators and their descendants – white Americans and Europeans. The necessity of overcoming our resistance to acknowledging and understanding this history in order that mourning can take place and wounds healed is emphasised.

The division into 'races' as justification for exploitation is developed further in Chapter 2 alongside confirmation from the Human Genome Project that there is no biological, essentialist basis to the concept. Racism precedes the notion of race and is deeply embedded in our political, economic and social structures. The case example of my work with a black patient, Dee, is used to illustrate how racism operates in the mind of the individual and within relationships. Consideration is given to how white clinicians need to be open to an exploration of our own racism in order that we can be available to work within a transference that will inevitably be complicated by the weight of racism.

Chapter 3 considers 'whiteness' from archetypal, empirical, imaginary and subjective perspectives. The concept of 'white privilege' is introduced with its invisibility, solipsism, colour blindness and ignorance, all of which serve to maintain the power differentials created between the centre and the margins in society. Robin DiAngelo's important concept of 'white fragility' is presented and illustrated with a case example of a teaching session. There is consideration of the price paid for this privilege, not only by those 'blackened' at the margins, but through the emotional impoverishment that results for white people in maintaining our privileged position at the centre.

Chapter 4 begins with a case example of work with Janet, a white patient who brought an instance of racist thinking to her analysis of which she was ashamed. The concepts of 'shame', 'guilt' and 'guiltiness' are discussed and, in consideration of how we learn our 'whiteness', a number of research projects on child development and racism are summarised. The evidence is that children learn racism at a very early age, but they also learn that it is not to be talked about. This, I suggest, is a consequence of the attitude of colour blindness in liberal adults and accompanying fragility which negates the realities of racism. This results in a vertical split in the psyche for the child which I refer to as the process of disavowal. The concept is developed with reference to Adrienne Harris's (2019) notion of the 'psychose blanche' which, in turn, develops Andre Green's (1970) concept of 'the dead mother'. The theory is then applied to the work with Janet.

Both Freud and Jung relied heavily on the early anthropologists of the nineteenth century, the 'armchair titans' who assumed a hierarchy of development with the black, so-called 'primitive' representing the 'uncivilised', unrepressed id contents of the Western psyche and the mind of the European infant. The implications for analytic theory are explored in Chapter 5. There is a focus on Jung in particular and the racist aspects of his theoretical position. The concept of the collective unconscious has value but is so large that the potential for abuse is considerable especially when – as was the case with Jung himself – the archetype and the stereotype become confused. The challenge of decolonisation of the theory is explored.

Chapter 6 explores the racism within modern day psychoanalytic and Jungian analytic institutions. Despite the research that has been undertaken regarding the experience of Black, Asian and Minority Ethnic trainees and members of the profession, we consistently fail to take the radical action to tackle racism. I suggest that there are aspects of our theoretical position as well as our training which make our institutions enclaves resistant to change. Part of this lies in our historic development. Part is a result of the distinction between 'inner' and 'outer' which runs through our theories. What I refer to as the 'myth of the complete analysis' may also be a factor. Possible ways forward are offered.

Power dynamics are often present in any supervisory relationship, especially when the supervisee is training, and the process of assessment is involved. A further layer of complexity is added when the supervisor is white and the supervisee black. The impetus to be the one who 'knows' means the supervisor may be unable to recognise and acknowledge the experience of the black trainee, who can then be seen as the one with the problem. When both are white and the patient is black, then anxiety may lead to the analytic attitude being compromised. Chapter 7 explores these dynamics using a number of case examples to illustrate how the supervisor needs to face and work with their own racism in order that the work may be deepened.

In Chapter 8 two examples of how racism operates are given – one rural and one urban – and explored further to understand the dynamics at play. The concepts of the *social unconscious* and the *cultural complex* are presented with particular reference to the racial complex as a way of thinking about deeply embedded racism and the maintenance of white privilege. The concept of the *perverse pact* is introduced as a way of formulating the contract between white people to maintain privilege and resist change.

In her book *In the Wake: On Blackness and Being*, Christina Sharpe (2016) builds on the three meanings of the concept of 'wake' and applies it to the hauntings of contemporary black lives. In the Epilogue I consider the significance of this idea for white people and for the work *we* need to do if we are to bring about change.

A plea

In his book *Partisans in an Uncertain World*, Paul Hoggett says:

> uncritical thought will not simply be passive but will actively cling to a belief in the appearance of certain things. It actively refuses, rejects as perverse or crazy, any view that may contradict it. To think critically one must therefore be able to use aggression to break through the limitations of one's own assumptions or to challenge the 'squatting rights' of the colonizer within one's own internal world.
>
> (1992, p. 29)

For those of us defined as belonging in the globally colonising white Western culture, can, if we choose, avoid external pressure to make that act of aggression that challenges the 'squatting rights' of the internal coloniser. But ignoring this figure who inhabits at least a corner of our minds demanding compliance does not mean he does not exist. I suggest we are the poorer if we do not attempt the act of aggression to break through our assumptions for they then remain an area of internal life that is unexamined. The stubbornness of the uncritical thought that actively clings to a belief in the appearance of certain things in Hoggett's quote may give us a clue to the tenacity of the fact of racism despite our wish that it were not so. For me to think differently about my place in the world and the privileges it has brought me requires an undoing of a well-laid system of assumptions about myself. The fact that those assumptions existed and continue to exist does not make me an inherently bad person, but to break through their limitations is hard work. This is a not an easy subject to 'play' with. It raises feelings of guilt, shame, envy, denial and defiance, all of which are hard enough to face in the privacy of one's own life. To explore it publicly can bring up in me a fear of getting it wrong, of saying the unforgivable and of exposing a badness in me.

Each 'white' person has their own relationship to 'whiteness'. Those who have grown up in societies with a colonial history carry a different collective cultural shadow than those who don't. The existence of the plantations and of institution-alised chattel slavery for several hundred years in the Americas leaves a different legacy than that inherited by the descendants of the European men who ran the trade. Few of us trace a direct hereditary line back to slavers; many have ances-tors who themselves were oppressed and discriminated against. Some experience discrimination now on the basis of gender language, class, sexuality, disability, etc. These personal histories and experiences are important and to be honoured and it is for each individual to find their own relationship to their ancestors and to their life story.

It is perhaps not surprising that we struggle to free ourselves just a little from the suffocating blanket of 'whiteness', assert our own subjectivity and apply a touch of colour. Because we are not taught to see ourselves in racial terms, and because the fact of racism challenges a benign sense of ourselves as 'good white people' (Sullivan, 2014), we employ a variety of defences to ward off accusations, including that of exceptionalism.

And yet . . . whatever our personal history, wherever we were born, into which class, however young or old we are, if we walk the world as 'white', we see our-selves reflected wherever we look. We may have to bear the discrimination due to our class or sexuality or gender or disability, but we do so without the added bur-den of racism. We do not fear the forces of law and order, doors are not closed to us because of our skin colour, and we have the choice to ignore or even deny rac-ism in the world we inhabit. Writing on 'white fragility', Robin DiAngelo (2018) makes a plea that when we face our whiteness, we need to set aside our sense of uniqueness. This, she says,

> is a critical skill that will allow you to see the big picture of the society in which we live; individualism will not. For now, try to let go of your indi-vidual narrative and grapple with the collective messages we all receive as members of a larger shared culture. Work to see how these messages have shaped your life, rather than use some aspect of your story to excuse yourself from their impact.

(p. 13)

I have attempted to look the concept and that of white privilege as full on as I can and it may not make an easy read. But I assume that people who choose to read this are likely to expect, even look for, a challenge to change. I echo DiAn-gelo's plea for engagement with the struggle, for it cannot be left to black people alone; we who are white must do our own work if we are to create a more just and fair society.

References

Brickman, C. (2018) *Race in Psychoanalysis. Aboriginal Populations in the Mind*. Oxon, NY: Routledge.

Cushman, P. (2000) White Guilt, Political Activity, and the Analyst: Commentary on Paper by Neil Altman. *Psychoanalytic Dialogues*, 10(4), 607–618.

Dalal, F. (2002) *Race, Colour and the Process of Racialization: New Perspectives from Group Analysis, Psychoanalysis and Sociology*. Hove, East Sussex: Brunner Routledge.

Davids, F. (2011) *Internal Racism: A Psychoanalytic Approach to Race and Difference*. Basingstoke: Palgrave Macmillan.

DiAngelo, R. (2018) *White Fragility: Why Its So Hard for White People to Talk About Racism*. New York: Beacon Press.

Gordon, P. (1993) Souls in Armour: Thoughts on Psychoanalysis and Racism. *British Journal of Psychotherapy*, 10(1), 62–76.

Green, A (1970) The Dead Mother. *On Private Madness*. London: Hogarth Press.

Harris, A. (2019) The Perverse Pact: Racism and White Privilege. *American Imago*, 76(3), 309–333.

Hoggett, P. (1992) *Partisans in an Uncertain World: The Psychoanalysis of Engagement*. London: Free Association Books.

MacMullan, T. (2009) *Habits of Whiteness. A Pragmatist Reconstruction*. Bloomington, IN: Indiana University Press.

Sharpe, C. (2016) *In the Wake: On Blackness and Being*. Durham, NC: Duke University Press.

Sullivan, S. (2006) *Revealing Whiteness. The Unconscious Habits of Racial Privilege*. Bloomington, IN: Indiana University Press.

Sullivan, S. (2014) *Good White People: The Problem with Middle-Class White Anti-Racism*. New York: State University of NY Press.

Chapter 1

Whiteness

In her challengingly titled book, *Why I'm No Longer Talking to White People About Race* (2017), Reno Eddo-Lodge states:

> At best, white people have been taught not to mention that people of colour are 'different' in case it offends us. They truly believe that the experiences of life as a result of their skin colour can and should be universal. I just can't engage with the bewilderment and the defensiveness as they try to grapple with the fact that not everyone experiences the world in the way that they do. They've never had to think about what it means, in power terms, to be white, so any time they're vaguely reminded of the fact they interpret it as an affront. Their eyes glaze over in boredom or widen in indignation. Their throats open up as they try to interrupt, itching to talk over you but not really listen, because they need to let you know that you've got it wrong.
>
> (pp. ix–x)

The concept of 'whiteness' as applied to humans is full of paradox and contradiction. No human being, even the fairest amongst us, has skin that is actually 'white', just as the darkest is not 'black'. Yet this crude form of colour coding which came into being in the modern era has divided humanity and ensured white supremacy in the service of domination, colonialism and slavery. Normalised into the default racial status permitting 'whites' to regard themselves as having no race, it has become both dominant and invisible. Invisible, at least, to those included within its borders, but not to those it excludes and who suffer its violence. As a racial category, 'white' is defined not so much by what it *is* but by what it is *not*. Hence the need for blackness, the racially codified 'other' which can hold the dark, the shadow, leaving white as pure, heavenly and innocent.

The Jungian analyst James Hillman (1986) notes that:

> Our culture, by which I mean the imagination, enactments and values collectively and unconsciously shared by Northern Europeans and Americans, is white supremacist. Inescapably white supremacist, in that superiority of

whiteness is affirmed by our major texts and is fundamental to our linguistic roots; and thus our perceptual structures. We tend to see white as best, as most embracing and define it in superior terms.

(p. 30)

'White' is a blanket term that erases all differences, all shades, hues and colours. Yet each white individual will have a unique relationship to the concept depending on history, geography, religion, ethnicity, class, gender, language, culture and more. A person of Irish, Southern European or Latin American descent, or those who are Jewish or from other minority religious groups, will have their own historic background of suffering and oppression. Indeed, there have been periods in times and places when each of these groups have been designated as 'non-white' or 'black'. There are also political and ethical differences within the white group. A white liberal will not have the same relationship to whiteness as will an avowed white supremacist.

There are those who argue for dispensing with the terms 'white' and 'black' altogether. The case has a logic in that, if the division is a meaningless, constructed one with no scientific basis, then repair and progress require us to drop these categories altogether and rely instead on the more nuanced one of ethnicity. The proposition is tempting but, in my view, dangerous, as it offers a shortcut which avoids the work that needs to be done if we are to reach a position of genuine equity in our world. It sidesteps the reality of the racist structures of our society which, in turn, allows us white folk to continue in our ways whilst also circumventing the discomfort that comes with the acknowledgement of our whiteness and the privileges to which it gives access. Relabelling those who suffer the iniquities of racism and oppression does not solve the problems of injustice and inequality. Whilst there are near infinite variations of individual stories which impact on our specific relation to whiteness, those of us who walk the world inside what is perceived to be a white skin have important matters in common. Whatever our personal history, wherever we were born, however young or old we are, if we are regarded as 'white' we have inherited layers of privilege and supremacy from which we benefit at the cost of others.

The sociologist Linda Alcoff (2015) identifies three key aspects of any social identity. These are:

- Its empirical status, or the ways in which an identity can be objectively located, measured and traced out historically in time and space.
- Its imaginary status, or the ways in which it constitutes a shared social imaginary that organizes and prescribes normative and accepted lifestyles, both for the in-group as well as for outsiders.
- Its subject-formation, or the constitution of individual subjects with particular ways of experiencing and perceiving as well as interacting with the social and natural environment.

(p. 74)

Empirical whiteness

Articulated as a category of social identity, whiteness 'was linked to an overt ideology of racial biologism, cultural vanguardism and the legitimation narratives of colonial conquest' (ibid, p. 76). Affirming its empirical status, she goes on to refer to

> the recent empirical scholarship on whiteness [which] is producing a rich trove of information on the history, the economics, the geography, the sociology, and the politics of white identity. Without a doubt, 'whiteness' as a category has an empirical referent.
>
> (p. 78)

In his introduction to *The Invention of the White Race. Vol 1*, Theodore Allen (1994) lays out the complexities of the history of 'whiteness'. The gathering of observable variations in human skin colour into the stark polarities of 'white' and 'black' emerged within the modern era. The deliberate use of this division for political and economic advantage seems to have been first recorded in seventeenth-century Virginia, when the first Africans arrived on slave ships to work the plantations. Anxious that the indentured European labour force would find common cause with the enslaved Africans, the use of the term 'white' was used to transform the masters, plantation owners and European labourers into one all-inclusive group. Through a set of laws that privileged whites alone, any class solidarity with the blacks was disrupted, ensuring that power remained in the hands of the ruling white elite.

Almost four centuries later, the divide between 'white' and 'black' continues as a powerful form of social partition that has torn through the history of humankind, harming individuals, groups, societies and relationships. Despite developments in scientific knowledge that dismantled the belief that there is an essential, biological difference between these categories, and despite social and political advances towards a more liberal agenda in much of the world, 'whiteness' remains a powerful socio-economic category which determines how societies are organised and power is distributed.

Imaginary whiteness

Alcoff questions the universality and individualism of a Freudian approach to the 'imaginary' in ego-formation and uses the term as a more collective, social concept which is based on a shared orientation which may have little to do with the historical facts. This perspective takes account of the societal dynamics – both conscious and unconscious – into which a child is born, alongside those that are familial or related to internal drives and object relations.

Bringing all those with lighter-hued skin within the rubric 'white' in the emergent, piecemeal way that this occurred not only allowed the illusion of common privilege but also tapped into our unconscious imaginary in relation to 'white' and to 'black'. These associations – albeit with some local variations – tend to be universal, based as they are in the nature of our bodies and the diurnal rhythms of the planet we inhabit. Mother's nourishing milk and father's productive sperm are white; bile and shit are black or brown. White is associated with the 'delights' of the daytime, the dove of peace and the pure soul, whereas black belongs to the dark terrors of night, to war and sin. Devils inhabit the blackness of Hell and angels the whiteness of Heaven.

This archetypal imagery has been elaborated by James Hillman (1986), who argues that the universality of these images means that, once the fair skinned were labelled as 'white' and all others 'black', the former were able to appropriate the 'goodness' of white, assigning the 'badness' of black to the rest. Through our language, our religions and our collective imaginings, we were archetypally prepared for white supremacy.

Hillman (1986) suggests that the archetypal uses of 'white' divide into three broad categories of meaning: as heavenly; as innocence; as anima or spirit. These are whitewashed categories which exclude the dark and the damaged so that any stain dissolves its purity. If colour is added then white ceases to be white, so distinctions, shades and tinctures are rejected as contaminating its purity. 'Innocence excludes: "innocent" literally denotes an absence of noxiousness, without harm or hurt. . . . Black becomes necessary to whiteness as that co-relative by means of which white takes on its defensive, exclusive definition as im-maculate, un-polluted, in-nocent' (p. 34).

When applied to humans, this has led to such absurdities as the 'one-drop test' – the social and legal policy in the US in the twentieth century which asserted that any person with even one ancestor of sub-Saharan ancestry is considered black. Or the 'pencil test' in South Africa to determine the curl of the hair, with all the racial and racist implications of apartheid.

This inability of white to include the imperfection of colour requires that the 'Other' is constellated so that the creation of 'whiteness' forces 'blackness' into existence and then turns distinctions into oppositions. Hillman points out that phenomena such as night and day, light and dark (or male and female) are different but not opposites. Since 'white' cannot allow dark to exist within itself, the shadow of whiteness must be rejected and cast into what it deems to be 'black'. Because what is cast out is the unacceptable and unwanted, it is assumed to exist as an opposite, and in opposition to itself. In Hillman's words:

> 'White casts its own white shadow'. This conclusion may be bettered to say, 'white sees its own shadow in black', not because they are inherently opposite but it is archetypally given to whiteness to imagine in oppositions. To say it again: *the supremacy of white depends on oppositional imagining.*
>
> (Ibid., p. 41. Italics in original)

Subjective whiteness

The assumption of whiteness as the default position of the human means that the individual may fail to notice that their whiteness affects their sense of identity and patterns of social interaction, taking for granted an entitlement to space, safety and freedom of movement. Such assumptions mostly go unacknowledged forming what Shannon Sullivan (2006) calls the '*unconscious habits*' of white privilege. Whilst not a term that appears often in the psychoanalytic discourse, Sullivan uses 'habit' to mean an unconscious interweaving of psychical and somatic aspects which contribute to the formation of the self. Approaching white privilege and racism from this angle, she argues that:

> Because habit is transactional, in a raced and racist world, the psychosomatic self necessarily will be racially and racistly constituted. Race is not a veneer lacquered over a nonracial core, it composes the very bodily and psychical beings that humans are and the particular ways by which humans engage with the world.
>
> (p. 24)

She goes on to say:

> The habit of ontological expansiveness enables white people to maximize the extent of the world in which they transact. But as an instance of white solipsism, it also severely limits their ability to treat others in respectful ways. Instead of acknowledging others' particular interests, needs, and projects, white people who are ontologically expansive tend to recognize only their own, and their expansiveness is at the same time a limitation.
>
> (p. 25)

I shall return to the discussion of the development of 'subjective whiteness' in a later chapter.

White privilege

Existing as it does on an individual, social, organisational and institutional level, white privilege brings a set of advantages which will include immunity from troubles that other groups may experience. It assumes access to, and unbiased treatment by, private and public institutions. It is being confident that we will be treated fairly by the criminal justice system, the health service, educational and other organisations, and knowing that when we introduce ourselves in a role of authority it will not be questioned. It is not having to be aware of being white the majority of the time and assuming our dress, speech and ways of behaving are racially neutral, when in fact they are white. We will see our own images in the media, in literature and the history books and take our representation there for granted. It is having the luxury to fight racism one day and ignore it the next.

White privilege does not require people's conscious awareness for it to exist; indeed its very invisibility is key to its continuance as it allows us the freedom to be blind to our own privilege. Thus we can benefit without having to acknowledge how our advantages depend on the disadvantage of others. Its hidden, implicit nature ensures its continuance as we remain 'innocent' of how our institutions and our social structures favour us as white people, ensuring that the racial hierarchy within society is perpetuated and maintained. Our inability (or refusal) to see how privileged our position is allows us not only to enjoy our racial advantages but to persist in defending them.

As Melanie Suchet (2007) puts it:

> Whiteness dominates through normalizing itself and constantly mutates while always maintaining supremacy. There are enormous variations of power among white people related to class, gender, sexuality, and other factors, and many ways to be white. Nonetheless, white power reproduces itself and can never be separated from privilege.
>
> (p. 869)

For the white working class, the notion of white privilege may feel an empty promise bearing little relationship to their lives. Those who suffer oppression, poverty and deprivation might find the idea leaves a bitter taste. Nevertheless, despite the caveats regarding the relationship of the working classes to white privilege, as DiAngelo (2018) argues, 'stating that racism privileges whites does not mean that individual white people do not struggle or face barriers. It does mean that we do not face the particular barrier of racism' (p. 24).

The centre and the margins

Writing about the dynamics of race, the psychoanalytic psychotherapist and group analyst Farhad Dalal (2002) refers to a discussion about colour that took place when he was training. His white supervisor said that he was not usually aware of the person's 'race' or colour in a session; it was not a significant issue for him. Dalal was struck by the contrast of his own experience as a man of Asian origins saying that he is 'often conscious in groups, and in one to one situations, of my colour in relation to others' (p. 219).

Dalal goes on to say:

> The white, by virtue of their colour, is in the mainstream and near the centre, whilst the black is marginalized and nearer the edge. The closer one is to the edge, with the resultant danger of going over, the more one is aware of the circumstances that put one there – colour. Meanwhile, those at the centre have a vested interest (often unconscious) in maintaining the status quo by blanking out the colour dynamic altogether: if it does not exist in the first place then it cannot be changed. Thus, the difference between the feelings elicited in me

and my supervisor are not just because of our asocial histories, but to do with where we are located in the field of power relations.

(p. 219)

We do not have single identities but are members of various societal groups simultaneously – groups that are defined by class, gender, sexuality, ethnicity, disability, religion, culture, language, etc. Each of these categories expresses a power dynamic within the social order and each defines the centre and its margins in relation to that split. Depending on which is foregrounded at any moment, we may find ourselves sometimes occupying the centre of the dynamic and sometimes the margins. In just one evening with friends, the discussion may move from class – where I would be located at the centre – to gender, where I am closer to the margins, and then to 'race', where I slide firmly back into the centre again.

My experience of those times when I am positioned more at the margins – such as when the subject under discussion is gender – is that it is from here that one has a much clearer view of the fact that a power dynamic exists and the form it takes. However, when someone describes the view from the edge, those at the centre often experience puzzlement and a sense of being unfairly accused, defensive and hostile.

Dalal (1998) notes that:

> The point about being at the margins is that the centre finds it hard to hear, partly because of psychological distance, and partly because what is being said is inconvenient. And so the marginalized are forced to shout until hoarse, and can end up sounding shrill. . . . Once 'whiteness' exists and is used to organize the social order, then blackness is forced into existence. The shape and meaning that this notion of blackness can take are constrained by what has been allocated to whiteness. The power of ideology is such that the 'whiteness' as organizing principle is unconscious. In other words, the white ensign at the centre is invisible, and it is only the black ensign at the margins that is able to be seen. Thus those at the centre feel themselves to be innocent, unfairly assaulted from without.

(p. 207)

White fragility

Robin DiAngelo (2018) makes a powerful argument for how this invisibility of whiteness and the privilege it brings contributes to what she calls 'white fragility'. She says,

> we are insulated from racial stress, at the same time that we come to feel entitled to and deserving of our advantage. Given how seldom we experience racial discomfort in a society we dominate, we haven't had to build our racial stamina. Socialized into a deeply internalized sense of superiority

that we either are unaware of or can never admit to ourselves, we become highly fragile in conversations about race. We consider a challenge to our racial worldviews as a challenge to our very identities as good, moral people. Thus, we perceive any attempt to connect us to the system of racism as an unsettling and unfair moral offense. The smallest amount of racial stress is intolerable – the mere suggestion that being white has meaning often triggers a range of defensive responses. These include emotions such as anger, fear, guilt and behaviours such as argumentation, silence and withdrawal from the stress-inducing situation. These responses work to reinstate white equilibrium as they repel the challenge, return our racial comfort, and maintain our dominance within the racial hierarchy. I conceptualize this process as *white fragility*. Though white fragility is triggered by discomfort and anxiety, it is born of superiority and entitlement. White fragility is not weakness per se. In fact, it is a powerful means of white racial control and the protection of white advantage.

(pp. 1–2. Italics in original)

DiAngelo draws attention to a familiar dynamic within whiteness which works to maintain the status quo. In my own experience, this formulation of white fragility describes well the discomfort and unease that quickly takes over when the topic of race and racism is raised.

I once visited a training organisation where guest clinicians were invited to teach a series of clinical seminars for trainees in order that they have the experience of a variety of clinical approaches within the psychoanalytic framework. In each seminar someone presented their work with a training patient for discussion. The group of trainees came from a variety of professions and they were experienced and able. Whilst of differing ages and backgrounds, we were all white.

In one seminar a trainee, Julie, described her work with a 40-year-old woman, Martha, who had come to the UK from South Africa. She had been referred because of her depression. Julie presented some details about the patient and the work to date including a process report of a particular session. The initial discussion was thoughtful and to the point, and it was apparent that Julie and her colleagues had a good grasp of analytic thinking. After a little while I realised that the patient's origins had barely been mentioned. I had assumed the patient was white but didn't know. So I asked and Julie told me the patient was black.

Immediately the tension in the room was palpable. The group, which until then had been working well together with everyone contributing to the thinking, froze. When I commented on this, one member of the group said she felt it was rude to ask about colour. The fear seemed to be that even raising the matter was possibly racist.

As someone noted regarding the part of the country in which they lived, 'there isn't much ethnic diversity in this part of Britain, so this feels somewhat alien to us'. As we discussed this further people began to express a fear of saying the 'wrong' thing or using the 'wrong' words, betraying a deep anxiety that racist thoughts might be exposed. The lack of racial stamina that DiAngelo describes was much in evidence. It began to be recognised that Julie – indeed all white therapists – had a responsibility to explore their own racism if it was not to infect the work. Gradually they could think about what it might mean for this black African woman living in such an area and now working with a white therapist, and recognised the need for the therapist to raise the fact of difference so it could be made available for thought. After much discussion it was suggested that Julie speak about the matter in a straightforward way within the narrative of the therapy.

Julie reported later that asking what she termed 'the white therapist question' had considerable impact on the work. She wrote:

> Although my patient seemed to dismiss its significance it was noticeable that she then brought material which was a) very culturally specific and b) which led to an increase in affect. Subjectively I felt in the session that there was a sense that the patient was able to entrust this new material with me.

Julie's regular supervisor also wrote to me:

> I too had really missed the point that the issue of a black patient and white therapist is something that needs to be spoken about in an ordinary way. . . . I can only agree that I also had a resistance to bringing up the issue. Resistance such as this, of course, is unconscious; it requires vigilance on the part of the profession. It has been good to see how well Julie took this on board and how helpful the patient found it and the therapy is progressing.

If the patient had been white, any failure to mention it would come from that aspect of white privilege that sees white as the default position – a form of white solipsism. My question made sense in the context that we had been told that the patient came from South Africa, but the assumption of whiteness was understandable given that the large majority of South Africans who have come to Britain and are likely to enter therapy are white. If the patient had been white, the therapist would have informed me of the fact, and we would have moved on without any of the difficulties that the whole group experienced. It is rude, it seems, not so much to raise the question of colour per se, but only when the individual is black. It is as if the brown skin is a deformity, a disability, an embarrassment which it is impolite to mention. In therapy, the colour muteness that results leaves a gap of silence which hushes up both an important aspect of the patient's lived experience and of the transferential relationship.

Colour blindness and white ignorance

In his explorations of the archetypal uses of whiteness, Hillman (1986) points out that the concept also implies attributes that are not so positive. White also represents what is ashen, pallid, colourless, blank, lily-livered, cowardly:

To the Greeks white-livered also meant simple-minded, silly, foolish (that is naïve) emotions, since the liver is the seat of darkblooded passions and of black bile in Greek imaginative physiology. A white-livered person, to fatten the metaphor, would have no stomach for fight (would show the white flag, the white feather, throw in the towel), no guts, no balls . . . no passion for darkness.

(p. 36)

He also writes of white as 'but a blank and ignorant page, the requisite stupidity at the start' (p. 34).

This emphasis on the ignorance of innocence echoes the invisibility and unawareness in whiteness that Dalal describes. The professed colour blindness of his supervisor suggests an insensitivity to the lived experience of the brown trainee to whom he is talking, a lack of awareness of the realities of racism and the implications for their relationship and a denial of his own privilege and hidden racist responses. In my experience, white people only fail to notice the colour of the other's skin colour when the person is white. When a black person is present – and especially when the subject for discussion is colour and racism – white people become highly alert to the difference. Strategies to avoid the anxiety that results include colour blindness by assuming difference is just not seen. Whilst this colour-blind position is often promoted as one that is non-racist and in accordance with liberal ideology, it reinforces white ignorance by shutting down curiosity and enquiry and, therefore, relationship. If we don't see 'race' then we can't see racism.

The philosopher Charles Mills refers to 'white ignorance' in his book *The Racial Contract* (1997):

The Racial Contract prescribes for its signatories an inverted epistemology, an epistemology of ignorance, a particular pattern of localized and global cognitive dysfunction (which are psychologically and socially functional), producing the ironic outcome that whites will in general be unable to understand the world they themselves have made.

(p. 18)

Alcoff (2015) refers to Mills's argument in relation to whites as 'a set of substantive epistemic practices designed to protect their belief that society is basically a meritocracy, people of colour are responsible for their troubles, and racism is a thing of the past' (p. 84).

Just as DiAngelo stresses that 'white fragility' is not a weakness but a way of protecting white privilege, 'white ignorance' is the means by which we at the centre close our eyes to our privilege and the impact on those at the margins. By staying blind and unknowing, by assuming racism, disparity and prejudice belong to the past or to a few individuals within modern day society, we manage the tightrope of relieving ourselves of guilt whilst ensuring the advantages of our whiteness are maintained.

It also cuts us off from curiosity about the other which, in turn, forms a barrier to relationship. I don't know how the conversation between Dalal and his supervisor developed, but the implication is that the latter's response ended the discussion. If so, the supervisor may have protected himself from discomfort, but he also missed out on the opportunity to explore the anxiety behind such a defence and to deepen his understanding of himself in relation to race and racism. It also shut down the possibility of enquiry into Dalal's experience as a person of colour managing a psychoanalytic training in a predominantly white organisation, as well as any concerns he has about possible responses by white patients to him as a therapist of Asian descent. The opportunity to explore the possible impact of difference within the supervisory relationship and Dalal's experience as a supervisee was also lost.

On one occasion I was presenting a paper on racism to an all-white group of therapists. The usual difficult and uncomfortable discussion followed in which the group seemed collectively engaged in finding ways to avoid the emotional work of exploring their own racism. These included individuals separating themselves from the white group by asserting a different nationality, language, history, class or age. Questions were asked as to why we were not focusing on sexuality, gender, class or disability – all important subjects but not the topic for the day. As it always does, the introduction of these other inequalities managed to flatten the discussion so the subject of racism was in danger of disappearing altogether. Someone pointed out that 'black people are racist too', managing to evade the critical matter of power differentials. The hostility towards me as the person raising the subject was palpable. It was a familiar but depressing event.

After some time, a woman who had been silent till then said she was thinking about an experience on her way to the seminar that day. She was waiting in her car at some traffic lights and another car pulled up beside her, driven by a woman dressed in a burqa. Looking across, the thought came to her: 'Oh! So they can drive, can they?' She had instantly pushed the thought away as she was aware of the racism behind it but had been turning the memory over in her mind throughout the discussion. As someone who usually experienced no difficulty in speaking in groups, she was puzzled by what felt like a profound reluctance to bring this thought into the discussion. She recognised her own internal condemnation of the prejudice tied up in the thought, as well as a fear of external attack were she to give it voice.

By recounting her thought to the group who until then were firmly in the 'I am not a racist' position, she articulated a different reality. In my experience, three main possibilities were then open to the group. The first was to isolate and scapegoat the individual, so she carried alone all the guilt of having racist thoughts. The second was to normalise her response and wipe it clean of any racism, thus bringing her over to their side of the divide. The third, which fortunately was what happened in this particular group, was for her courage to give permission for others to recall similar instances in their own lives. The atmosphere shifted, the anxiety and the defensiveness became less intense and the level of communication deepened. There emerged the chance of ownership of just a little of the destructiveness of our racism, allowing the possibility of grief.

Bion's 'minus K'

Bion describes the links that define the emotional experience that is ever present when two people or two parts of a person are in relation to each other. These 'links' comprise Love (L), Hate (H) and Knowledge (K). Whereas L and H are rooted more in the paranoid-schizoid position, K is seen as an aspect of the depressive position. 'The sign K . . . is used to refer to the link between a subject which tries to know an object, and an object which can be known' (Grinberg, 1985, p. 64).

The K link refers to the process of relating where one gets to know another in an emotional sense. It is to be distinguished from *knowing about*, of having a piece of knowledge or learning some facts about someone or something. The more paranoid-schizoid links of L and H within racism might be tempered by those of K. It is not blind to colour but admits an awareness of the political and social backdrop to our encounter with each other. It acknowledges difference in colour and, therefore, a difference in experience and hence in vertex or perspective.

To fail to acknowledge difference, to assume colour blindness, leads us more into the realm of –K: Whereas 'K' symbolises knowledge, –K represents not only ignorance, but an active avoidance of awareness where the truth would disadvantage the individual or the group were they allow themselves to 'know'. Just as 'K' is not a mere knowing of facts, '–K' is not the state of not-knowing the fact.

Whites have no need to see and hear the experiences of those who are black. More than that, in order that we might protect our privileged status, it is in our interest to remain deaf, dumb and blind to the disparities and inequalities. Through our so-called colour blindness we perpetuate our ignorance of – we ignore – the reality of that privilege and of our own racism. White fragility freezes our curiosity and silences our capacity to have ordinary conversations and to hear about a black individual's experience. This is hardly conducive to relationship.

Mills (2007) argues that as a consequence of 'white ignorance' there is an asymmetry between the perspectives of whites and those of blacks. He points out that: 'Often for their very survival, blacks have been forced to become lay anthropologists studying the strange culture, customs, and mind-set of the "white tribe" that has such frightening power over them' (p. 17).

In a footnote to his 2011 paper, Stephen Hartman describes the following incident:

> Back when I was in graduate school learning how to administer a mental status exam, my classmates and I were shown a graying video of a woman with schizophrenia being interviewed in a state hospital. . . . The African American (then negro) woman is insisting that she has a firm grasp of reality and that the interviewer has no right to be holding her against her will. She argues, 'I know it like Martin Luther King knew it. He *k*-knew it, knew it with a *k*, the kind of *k* you don't say, the kind of *k* that you don't say when you know what the white man don't want you to know. Martin Luther King knew. He *k*-knew it – knew it with a *k*. The *k* you're not allowed to say. And they got him'.

Then as now, I was amazed by the poetry of the truth she, however dis-traught and disorganized, had ripped from language: the silent *k* of discursive knowledge, the *k* you're not allowed to say. Not quite Bion's *k*, a *k* on the way to knowledge. . . . Rather a lost *k*, silenced by the power aggregated in race and segregated from knowledge by the bars of reality testing. This 'k' that you don't say holds the realities of racism that normal reality disavows. More akin to Bion's *negative 'k'* the silent 'k' before NO evacuates insight to regulate knowledge. It dilutes and, perhaps, attacks our ability to link reality and authority. On screen, the interviewer nodded to the camera and a voice-over instructed us that the flight of ideas demonstrated in this woman's word salad was evidence of her failed reality testing.

(p. 471)

For this 'white tribe', through our 'ignorance' and our 'fragility', we may hang on tight to our privilege but the cost is high. High for those who are black or brown who not only have to suffer the disadvantage, racism and iniquities of this system, but also our distaste and lack of resilience, our refusal to acknowledge the problem and engage. But it also seems an emotionally impoverished place for us white people to live, for the determination to protect the 'purity' and 'innocence' of whiteness, also promotes a blank, lily-livered and dreary emptiness. We have all learnt our whiteness and it goes deep. But I, for one, want my colour back.

References

Alcoff, L.M. (2015) *The Future of Whiteness*. Cambridge: Polity Press.

Allen, T. (1994) *The Invention of the White Race*. London & New York: Verso.

Dalal, F. (1998) *Taking the Group Seriously*. London: Jessica Kingsley.

Dalal, F. (2002) *Race, Colour and the Process of Racialization: New Perspectives from Group Analysis, Psychoanalysis and Sociology*. Hove, East Sussex: Brunner Routledge.

DiAngelo, R. (2018) *White Fragility. Why It's So Hard for White People to Talk About Racism*. New York: Beacon Press.

Eddo-Lodge, R. (2017) *Why I'm No Longer Talking to White People About Race*. London and New York: Bloomsbury Circus.

Grinberg, L. (1985) *Introduction to the Work of Bion*. London: Karnac (First published in 1975 by the Roland Harris Educational Trust).

Hartman, S. (2011) Reality 2.0: When Loss Is Lost. *Psychoanalytic Dialogues*, 21(4), 468–482.

Hillman, J. (1986) Notes on White Supremacy. Essaying an Archetypal Account of Histori-cal Events. *Spring Publications*, 29(56), 29–58.

Mills, C. (1997) *The Racial Contract*. Ithaca, NY: Cornell University Press.

Mills, C. (2007) White Ignorance. *Race and Epistemologies of Ignorance*. Eds: Sullivan, S., and Tuana, T. Albany, NY: State University of New York Press.

Suchet, M. (2007) Unraveling Whiteness. *Psychoanalytic Dialogues*, 17(6), 867–886.

Sullivan, S. (2006) *Revealing Whiteness. The Unconscious Habits of Racial Privilege*. Bloomington, IN: Indiana University Press.

Chapter 2

The legacy of slavery

The legacy of three hundred years or so of the transatlantic slave trade – often referred to as the African Holocaust – is a familiar subject for study and grieving by those who are descended from the enslaved. The suffering of the millions of those who died in captivity haunts current generations of those who are black, as Saidya Hartman (2007) portrays in her powerful description of her journey along the Atlantic slave route of her ancestors. She says:

> If the past is another country, then I am its citizen. I am the relic of an experience most preferred not to remember, as if the sheer will to forget could settle or decide the matter of history. I am a reminder that twelve million crossed the Atlantic Ocean and the past is not yet over. I am the vestige of the dead. And history is how the secular world attends to the dead.
>
> (pp. 17–18)

To date this is a mostly one-sided affair, as we who are the descendants of the slavers and the beneficiaries of the profits of the trade by virtue of our whiteness consistently deny and fail to recognise the hauntings of our legacy. For us, too, the past is not yet over.

In Steve McQueen's 2013 film *Twelve Years a Slave*, the kidnapped freeman Solomon Northrop (Chiwetel Ejiofor) has been taken South along with others including Eliza (Adepero Oduye) and her two children. We witness a shocking depiction of a slave auction where white gentry inspect naked men and women as if it were a cattle market. The plantation owner William Ford (Benedict Cumberbatch) wants to purchase Northrop (renamed Platt) and Eliza (she is given no other name) but cannot afford to buy her children as well, so they will be sold off to another plantation despite Eliza's desperate pleading. She and her children are separated, she can offer them no further protection and they will never see each other again.

In the next scene Ford arrives home with Northrop and Eliza in the back of the cart. Eliza is beside herself with grief. Ford's wife (Liza Bennett) comes out to see what he has bought and asks why Eliza is crying. When Ford explains she says, 'Oh dear. Poor, poor woman'. She pauses and looks genuinely sorry for

Eliza. Then she says, 'Something to eat and some rest. Your children will soon be forgotten'.

Eliza keeps weeping. It is her only form of protest against the violence that has been done to her and her family. A little later we watch Ford reading the Bible at a Sunday gathering while his wife shows irritation at the noise Eliza is making. We next see Eliza leaving the plantation, having been sold off to another master and another mistress.

The film follows the travails of Northrop and depicts ever more extreme acts of brutality, rape and humiliation on the enslaved Africans by white men and their wives. The intensity of humiliation, intimacy and extreme sadism that was involved in these interactions have a raw, primal feel to them and we want to look away. But perhaps for the white audience our horror, whilst real, keeps us apart from and disidentified with these white others. This was another time, another place, another morality from which we distance ourselves.

The scene on the steps of the Ford plantation shows no whippings, no acts of mortification, no sexual abuse, but is chilling nonetheless. As Mrs Ford watches Eliza weep, we are allowed for just a moment the possibility of compassion from one woman for another to enter the scene. 'Poor, poor woman' she says, and a gap opens up in this terrible narrative for the white audience to imagine ourselves there, to identify, and in that identification we are offered a moment of humanity in this portrayal of whiteness. Mrs Ford's follow up words, her dismissal of Eliza's agony, snaps the gap shut and leaves us defenceless.

This failure by one mother to identify with another and to know that this is a grief from which you *never* recover is deeply disturbing. Presumably, behind Mrs Ford's failure to recognise and have compassion for Eliza's pain is a belief that the same depth of mother-child attachment does not apply to Eliza, who is regarded as less than fully human. Realistically she could not think otherwise; the humanity of the other must be disavowed if she is to continue her life as the wife of a slave owner. The inhumanity, of course, is in the white woman's lack of capacity for compassion and concern.

Europe before the transatlantic slave trade

As is the case in most parts of the globe, the practice of slavery has been an accepted feature of European life at least since Classical times. Any substantial and widespread objection to the practice is a relatively recent phenomenon despite liberalising movements throughout history. In *The Problem of Slavery as History*, Joseph Miller (2012) points out that:

> Over more than two millennia of Western history . . . slavery had flourished at the very moments most celebrated in the Western tradition of freedom. These paradoxical combinations of slavery and freedom included classical Athens, otherwise known for democracy; the Roman Empire's civilizing of barbarian north western Europe; fifteenth-century Florence at the height of

Renaissance humanism; and eventually in the Americas at the very birth of modern civic freedoms. How could these champions of the story of Western progress toward modern human rights not have recognized the obvious need to eliminate the inhumanity of human bondage?

(p. 13)

It seems the human mind has the capacity to *both* hold an ideal of freedom *and* justify the fact of slavery.

Throughout European history the division of humanity that licensed one group to enslave another was actively supported by the philosophy of the day. Assuming differences in human bodies and souls, Aristotle argued that humanity was split between free men and those who lacked certain capabilities and were, therefore, fit for 'natural slavery'. Slavery appears in the Koran and the Old and New Testaments and was advocated by such figures as St Augustine and Thomas Aquinas, both of whom saw the enslaved state as a punishment for sin.

Transatlantic slavery

The transatlantic triangular trade began in the fifteenth century with the Portuguese the main players in early explorations:

> In the 1430s and 1440s, successive voyages pressed further south along the African coast, at each point touching on internal African trade routes which yielded goods (and humanity) from deep inside Africa. The early slaves taken to Portugal were Arab, Berber and black African. In 1444 the first batch were displayed in a field outside Lagos in southern Portugal.
>
> (Walvin, 2007, p. 37)

The British entered the trade in 1562 when John Hawkyns sailed from England, captured several hundred Africans off the coast of Sierra Leone and took them to what is now known as the Dominican Republic. He returned with a cargo of ivory, hides and sugar. Back in London Queen Elizabeth stated: '[i]f any African were carried away without their free consent it would be detestable and would call down vengeance from heaven upon the undertakers' (Hazlewood, 2004, p. 91). It seems, however, this moral outrage, this initial, instinctive human revulsion was soon quelled when she came to realise the extent of the profits to be made. She provided Hawkyns with a ship, 'The Good Ship Jesus', and sent him back to Africa with her royal blessing. This was, perhaps, the first official act of disavowal permitting British involvement in and eventual domination of the trade.

Prior to the use of enslaved Africans there was virtually no link between slavery and 'blackness', until the transatlantic trade whereby slaves began to be marked as of a different, darker skin colour. Africans lived in Britain during Roman times as soldiers and slaves, but also as free men and women. According to Miranda Kaufmann, author of *Black Tudors: The Untold Story* (2017), by Tudor times black people were present in small numbers in the English royal courts from Henry VII to James I and lived and worked at many levels of society. They were acknowledged as citizens and, importantly, were baptised, married and buried in the church. Tudor England before the involvement in the slave trade was

> an island nation on the edge of Europe with not much power, a struggling Protestant nation in perpetual danger of being invaded by Spain and being wiped out. . . . The English colonial project only really gets going in the middle of the 17th century.

She asks: 'How did we go from this period of relative acceptance to become the biggest slave traders out there?' (*Guardian* interview, by Bidisha, Oct 29, 2019).

Once the idea of the 'races' was established with the black regarded as 'primitive' and the white as 'civilised', there could develop a justification of colonisation and slavery of the former by the latter. Celia Brickman (2018) notes that:

> When Columbus set sail for the Indies and found himself instead in the New Worlds, already in place were two distinct frameworks for comprehending outsiders. The first was a medieval literary and popular discourse about outsiders as barbarians, wild men and noble savages, while the second was a religious-legal discourse, consolidated during the Crusades, concerning the treatment of infidels and the lawful right of Christians to the confiscation of uninhabited and non-Christian lands.
>
> (pp. 19–20)

The 'Wild Man' was a frightening object who, unrestrained by 'civilised' laws, could give full rein to his passions. The 'Noble Savage', on the other hand, still lived in the Garden of Eden and represented a lost paradise of innocence and peace which existed before Europeans were burdened with the demands of civilisation. 'The contrasting images of the Wild Man and the Noble Savage . . . contributed to a contradictory discourse which represented non-Europeans as both idealized and depraved, fulfilled in their simplicity yet lacking in their humanity' (Ibid., p. 21).

There are no certain statistics of how many individuals were taken from Africa in the centuries since the first ship set sail from Portugal, but the number is estimated to be well over ten million, about a quarter of whom were children. This figure does not include the many who died on the journey – probably about three in ten. Deaths were also inflicted in the process of capture as well as through disease brought by the Europeans and the destruction of the existing economic basis for living. Nor does the number take account of all the generations born into slavery who never knew freedom throughout their entire lifetime.

Whereas old-world slave communities tended to be static so that families and kinship systems could be sustained, in the Americas slave groups and families were often broken up with slaves sold on to other plantations, disrupting the most intimate of relationships and violating the most human of taboos. Men were used as studs but often allowed little in the way of relationship with the women or their children. Women were frequently raped by white masters which their own men were powerless to do anything about. The bonds, between men and women, between mothers and fathers and their children, were broken when slaves were sold on to other plantations. Their bodies were not their own – nor were those of their children.

It is this wide-scale and continuous severing of intimate bonds and the defilement of basic taboos which marks out the dreadful psychological devastation of slavery; a devastation which carried on for several centuries. Bodily wounds may heal, and losses can be grieved, but there are some forms of desecration of the fundamental nature of our humanity that can only be survived by the construction of powerful psychological defences.

Transgenerational trauma

Studies of the long-term psychological effects of such catastrophic social periods as the European Holocaust and Stalinism have led to an understanding of how the effects of trauma, if not sufficiently acknowledged and worked through, can be inherited by future generations. Unconscious defences, established as a means of surviving the trauma, can prevent loss from being taken in, integrated and transformed. Instead the damage is incorporated as a blockage which causes stasis and paralysis. In this inorganic, unabsorbed form, it cannot die with those who suffer the trauma but is passed on like a dreadful, undigested legacy to the next generations.

As Stephen Frosh (2013) points out: 'One of the things that Holocaust scholarship has demonstrated is how strongly a trauma lived through in one generation continues to have effects in later ones' (p. 2). The metaphor of the ghost, of phantoms and haunting, is one many writers use to describe this process. Frosh goes on to say:

> To be haunted is more than to be affected by what others tell us directly or do to us openly; it is to be influenced by a kind of inner voice that will not stop speaking and cannot be excised, that keeps cropping up to trouble us and stop us going peaceably on our way. It is to harbour a *presence* that we are aware of, sometimes overwhelmed by, that embodies elements of past experience and future anxiety and hope, and that *will not let us be*.
>
> (pp. 2–3. Italics in original)

Nicolas Abraham and Maria Torok (1994) explore this phenomenon in their book *The Shell and the Kernel*. They supplement Freud's theory of *dynamic repression* which is based on a desire to be rid of censored emotions with a process they call *preservative repression*. If the initial trauma or series of traumatic events cannot be spoken of, then what is lost – the loved object or the loved self – cannot be acknowledged and grieved. There is a failure of mourning. Instead, the unwanted, unexpressed emotions are sealed off within the psyche so that the traces of an obliterated event are preserved yet hidden from consciousness. Buried in silence, the unbearable memories and emotions are entombed in *psychic crypts* within the unconscious.

These crypts hold the secrets of the initial experience of trauma and become a burial place for what is lost. What has been lost is not mourned but kept inside the psyche like a living corpse. Through silent unconscious communication the buried objects are passed down from parent to child so that the lives of future generations become haunted by the tragedies of the ancestors. It becomes a form of 'unthought knowledge' (Bollas, 1987).

When a trauma takes place on a collective scale and there is no space for shared mourning, unspoken memories are forced into tombs within the cultural uncon-scious of whole communities, societies and nations. These crypts then become part of the background atmosphere into which new generations are born. Individ-uals, only hazily aware of their inheritance, may display symptoms which seem to have no direct personal cause. Unconsciously 'known', but unspoken so unavail-able for thought, they have a powerful impact on the way the culture views itself.

Sam Kimbles (2014) develops the notion of the psychic crypt, and introduces the hypothesis that intergenerational processes 'are manifested as *phantom nar-ratives* that provide structure, representations and continuity for unresolved or unworked-through grief and violence that occurred in a prior historical context that continues into the present' (p. 21). He says the phantom narratives provide an affective field which

> has a narrative structure with (quoting Chomsky, 1968) 'deep and buried con-tents' that operates at the level of the cultural unconscious and is structured by the cultural complexes. . . . I employ the term to open a new kind of imaginative space for reflecting on the changes and impacts that our cur-rent historical situation brings to us as context and content for adaptation and growth at both the group and individual levels. It is the unbearable, the too-muchness, the untranslatable, the felt presence of absence that opens the space for phantom narratives.
>
> (p. 17)

Kimbles sees these phantom narratives as contained within what he describes as 'cultural complexes'. Fanny Brewster (2020) posits the notion of the racial com-plex as a particular form of cultural complex and writes of her relationship as an African American to the legacy of slavery:

> I feel that as people of color it took us so very long to arrive at this destination in this time when we can almost touch, not yet fully embrace our historical trauma. It sometimes still hurts too much as an individual and as someone belonging to the culture of ancestral slavery. The centuries that we were born into and lived in human bondage are a part of our historical, intergenerational

trauma. We have barely begun to hear ourselves and hear our own voices awakening to the trauma.

(p. 27)

Legacy for the descendants of enslaved Africans

It is not my place as a white woman to theorise about the possible inheritance for descendants of those who were enslaved, so I turn, instead, to the work of black colleagues and writers.

Toni Morrison's novel *Beloved* (1987) is based on the real-life story of Margaret Garner, an enslaved woman who escaped with her four children from the Kentucky plantation 'Sweet Home'. When a posse arrived to return them, she attempted to murder her children, succeeding in ending the life of her 2-year-old daughter. After a lifetime of sexual abuse and knowing the fate of her children were they to be returned to the plantation, death was preferable to enslavement – and infanticide a desperate form of love.

The novel is set years after these events when the central character, Sethe, is visited by a woman called Beloved, who is presumed to be her daughter. She has returned to haunt Sethe's home in Cincinnati.

In the following extract, Sethe's lover, Paul D, has been challenged by her daughter, Denver, who she then defends:

> Risky, thought Paul D, very risky. For a used-to-be-slave woman to love anything that much was dangerous, especially if it was her children she had settled on to love. The best thing, he knew, was to love just a little bit, so when they broke its back, or shoved it in a croaker sack, well, maybe you'd have a little love left over for the next one.
>
> (p. 54)

As Gabriele Schwab (2010) points out:

> It is not only Sethe's personal history as a slave that triggers the killing of her baby daughter; it is also the history of her own mother, who was never allowed to keep any of her children. Sethe's mother passed down to her the sense that it is better to be dead than a slave and better as a slave not to attach yourself even to your children the way a free mother would.
>
> (p. 79)

Brewster (2019) explores the archetypal grief of child loss for enslaved African women and how it has been handed down through the generations. She suggests that:

> because of the traumatic nature and longevity of this type of grief, due to centuries of American slavery – cultural trauma – it has become powerful

and reflective of centuries-long archetypal *potentiality* that becomes active at a cross-generational level. Furthermore, I am suggesting that this *potentiality* becomes realized in the behaviour and lived experiences of people of color. The historical presence of slavery and its profound effect on African Americans has supported the development of a psychic state showing itself as an *ever-present grief* through generations.

(p. 4. Italics in original)

Barbara Fletchman Smith, a British psychoanalytic psychotherapist, has explored the possible impact of the history of slavery on certain sections of the modern black population in her books, *Mental Slavery* (2000) and *Transcending the Legacies of Slavery* (2011). She notes that:

Slavery's longest-lasting legacy is the dominant family structure that it shaped. There is no escaping the fact that slavery determined how the family formed in the Caribbean, and its repercussions are still with us today. . . . Present day problems with forming couples and making and maintaining families have everything to do with the historical past of the individual and society. Slavery by its nature was responsible for the introduction of a deficit in maternal care, combined with the introduction of excessive fear into the mind.

(2011, p. xii)

Using clinical material from her own work, Fletchman Smith discusses the distorted Oedipal Complex that would have been inevitable within Caribbean plantation society where the family and its fundamental intimate bonds were constantly disrupted:

The sexual abuse endured by women at the hands of slave owners, in the knowledge that their own men could not save them, created distrust, hatred and contempt but also pity for their men that can still be observed in the present.

And:

Slavery was intended to wipe out male power and split maternity and paternity from procreation. It dictated a direction from which a new kind of family would develop.

(Ibid., p. 4)

Fletchman Smith suggests that the consequences of such violations of the fundamental human bonds are felt today in some black communities when women find their strength in gathering together around the motifs of the strong black woman and the feckless man. This, she argues, originates in, and has been handed down from, the plantations, where their men, castrated by the system, could not be relied on. Such contempt for the 'babyfathers' may be unconsciously communicated to the children. The girls learn to perpetuate the vilification of men, and the boys struggle in relationship to their own masculinity. This can result in a repetition of the pattern as they turn away from the disparaging females and look instead towards other males to find a form of intimacy and expression of potency via the gang culture.

Fletchman Smith (2000) stresses that these are extreme forms of expression of slavery's legacy and are by no means enacted in all modern black individuals and groups. As she points out:

> As in all situations in which there are perpetrators and victims, it is what the victims do in their own minds with the horrors they experience that – to a large extent – determines the future state of mind of that individual. This explains why some people not only survived, but have thrived in spite of the experience of slavery. Others have not been so fortunate.
>
> (p. 7)

In her later book (2011), she remarks that:

> The process of turning a person into a slave, who then suffers from mental slavery and passes it on down the generations through internalisation, can cause us such conceptual giddiness that thinking itself becomes burdensome. But it has to be thought about, if there is to be improvement in the care of people who are suffering psychologically and physically in their daily lives as the long-term result.
>
> (2011, p. xii)

Legacy for the perpetrators

Gabriele Schwab (2010) writes of the '*haunting legacy*' of the Holocaust of the twentieth century from the perspective of a contemporary German woman. She also suggests that, even though the slave trade is further back in time and we are several more generations on, the same mechanisms apply. As Abraham and Torok (1994) put it:

> it is reasonable to maintain that the 'phantom effect' progressively fades during its transmission from one generation to the next and that, finally, it disappears. Yet this is not at all the case when shared or complimentary phantoms find a way of being established in social practice.
>
> (p. 176)

The persistence of racism throughout our societies is such a social practice.

Miller (2012) warns us against using our horror of slavery as a defence, noting that:

> In view of the subsequent histories of civic exclusion by gender, race and other discriminatory social categories, slavery as an institution has remained a convenient target, not least because – for well-intended progressives – it was nearly always presented as someone else's problem, and, as institution-alised, it could be, and was, abolished.
>
> (p. 17)

In his paper 'Slavery in the White Psyche' (2019), Ryan Parker notes that in the US slavery is considered to be black people's history which he says 'screams of disavowal' (p. 5) on the part of the white population. Instead he hypothesises that 'slavery – as historical reality, signifier and symbol – has deep psychological implications for contemporary white Americans' (p. 1). His research into the matter involved lengthy interviews with nine women and six men between the ages of 28 and 74 about their attitudes to the subject.

All of his participants recalled little to no learning about slavery at school, where the attitude was, yes it was bad, but in the past, so there was no point in talking about it except for the fact that it ended. When asked to report any visual images that come to mind when they thought about slavery, 'Several participants' internal images focused on the sentimental and/or fantastically benign images of slaves "picking cotton", "serving lemonade", "living in the guesthouse"' (p. 10). Parker suggests such images are remnants of the literature, theatre and films of the late nineteenth to mid-twentieth centuries, with *Gone With the Wind* (1939) as 'the prototypical example of this narrative' (p. 10).

However, the more prominent images were ones of violence: tortured black bodies, rape and castration. Absent from the description were any white bodies who perpetrated these violent acts: 'The closest some participants got was a reference to "they" or to a weapon of terror: a "whip" or a "flaming torch"' (p. 10).

Parker suggests that:

> In addition to the refusal of black subjectivity and the invisible maintenance of white supremacy that these images *effect*, they also provide for their current bearer a conscious feeling of being a *horrified witness*. I am beginning to think this has a powerful defensive role in whiteness at large. Horrified, one can stay frozen in a state of disbelief, powerless, neither victim nor perpetrator. As the petrified bystander, one is able to keep a 'safer' identificatory distance from both. . . . In other words, in highlighting slavery's heinous violence, there is an unconscious wish to disidentify with its perpetrators, who remain disembodied, unseen and unnamed. This defensive function is an attempt to disavow an identification with the aggressor; to imagine oneself safely on the other side of history, so to speak; to imagine revulsion rather than complicity.
>
> (pp. 11–12. Italics in original)

The defensive nature of whiteness was most in evidence when Parker asked the participants the question: 'What do you think it might have been like to be born into a slave-owning family?' (p. 14). Many 'misheard' the question and imagined instead what it would be like to be born a slave and described scenes of violence, rape and subjugation. Where individuals were able to envision themselves as plantation owners – all as adults – they mostly assumed they would be 'good' slave owners or actively help the slaves to escape. The position of the white child seemed almost impossible to conceptualise. The tension between an aversion to slavery and a loyalty to imagined slave-owning parents was too great and the imagination broke down.

Parker was struck by the way the participants moved from fantasies of suffering extreme cruelty and violence when identified with the slave, to images of themselves as benign masters. One participant acknowledged that as a plantation owner he would probably have seen the slave as property like an animal, but he 'becomes a benevolent slave master who "would try to be extremely kind" by not mistreating or killing "them" but would feed, clothe, and take care of them so they will perform' (p. 17).

This report comes straight after the same participant had spoken of the violence he imagines would have been inflicted on him when in the position of the slave:

> Where is the mind of the master who hunts and hangs? It is this master who is suspiciously absent (completely erased) from the participant's two worlds and many participants' violent internal representations of slavery overall. The master is, of course, presumed, but vanished. The master is there but not there – disavowed.
>
> (p. 17)

Europe and the slave trade

Throughout the centuries of this terrible trade the fates of enslaved Africans and white Westerners have become profoundly entangled. This was physical, intimate and direct on the plantations of the Americas, but those from trading nations such as Britain were also deeply implicit in this collective trauma.

Miller (2012) urges us to view the transatlantic slave trade as part of a whole social process and not just as a relationship between the enslaved as one-dimensional victims of the similarly one-dimensional brutal masters with the whip as the dominating symbol. The plantations and chattel slavery became a key aspect of life in the Americas, but it was also deeply woven into the social fabric of the trading nations. In Britain the trade was an integral and important part of society at the time – even for those who had no direct involvement.

Slave ship owners were not all single merchants. Many small tradesmen had shares in a ship and in the ownership of the slaves that were captured so that, providing the ship didn't capsize or the slaves die on the way, a considerable profit was to be made.

Even for those who did not risk such a flutter in the trade, it permeated every-where in society – sometimes quite literally. In his novel, *The Quality of Mercy* (2012) set in eighteenth-century Britain, Unsworth describes how the main char-acter, Kemp, recalls his childhood visiting the Liverpool docks with his father:

> Smells of tar and molasses, and the smell of the slave ships waiting to be loaded with trade goods, a smell unlike any other, a dark odour of blood and excre-ment: the timbers were impregnated with it, no amount of scrubbing or sluicing had been able to take that smell away. . . . It had not even been necessary to visit the dock for it, he suddenly remembered; at times it had lain over the whole town. On certain days in summer, with the breezes coming from the west, it had invaded the houses, dark, indefinite, all-pervasive, entering parlours through open windows, contending with the scents of flowers in the gardens.
>
> (pp. 95–96)

The extent and endurance of the slave trade and colonisation and their critical place in the economic development of the West should not be underestimated. It was not merely a matter of an historical aberration. A 2005 BBC documentary, *The Empire Pays Back*, emphasised that profits from the trade was only a part of the story. The cities of London, Glasgow, Liverpool and Bristol grew substantially and European economies were transformed and expanded as a result of the trade and of the slave plantations in the Americas.

The important point here is that, like colonialism, the transatlantic slave trade was not a small-scale industry taking place on the edges of society involving a few traders and sailors. Nor was it just a matter for the plantations on the other side of the Atlantic. Nor can it be safely confined to historical records. For a trading nation such as Britain it was woven into life at all levels and remains visible today in buildings, monuments and institutions. Visible, that is, should we choose to see.

Mourning and melancholia

Those who have theorised about the phenomenon of inter-generational trauma suggest that the only way that the sins of the past will cease to haunt the present and future generations is for them to be brought into the open and worked through. Abraham and Torok (1994) call

> for a kind of psychoanalytic 'cult of ancestors' . . . that allows the dead to rest and the living to gain freedom from their ghostly hauntings. Yet to achieve this freeing from the past requires one first to awaken the dead and to revisit the trauma. This process is what we commonly call mourning. To facilitate a collective mourning, communities and nations develop the need to establish a culture of memory. Recognising the psychic life of our ancestors in our own psychic life means uncovering their unspoken suffering and secret histories, as well as their guilt and shame.
>
> (p. 79)

The damage done over centuries to generations of enslaved Africans gathers into a sustained trauma for individuals, families and societies and lies deep within the collective. There is much to be mourned. However, the impact on the descendants of victims and those of perpetrators is profoundly asymmetrical and the work of each is different. The descendants of the enslaved are burdened with the anguish of lives abused and cut short with all the grief and anger that results; the white population carries the unspoken, unacknowledged shame and guilt of the perpetrators.

> It is for good reason that psychoanalytic writing about whiteness and white racialization often turns on theories of trauma and intergenerational transmission. However, the distorted structures of self, inherited through whiteness should not be equated with the traumatic lineage of massive historical trauma for the victims and their descendants for whom our available theories have been developed. We need new theories to help us make sense of the distorted construction of self embedded in . . . whiteness – both in its history and ongoing perpetration, domination, and privileged complicity.
>
> (Parker, 2019, p. 17)

Exploring her relationship to the Holocaust as a German woman, Gabrielle Schwab (2010) suggests that the 'transgenerational transmission of collective guilt' is 'the identity trouble of children of perpetrators' (p. 95). She stresses that

> To facilitate a collective mourning, communities and nations develop the need to establish a culture of memory. Recognizing the psychic life of our ancestors in our own psychic life means uncovering their unspoken suffering and secret histories, as well as their guilt and shame, their crimes.
>
> (p. 79)

Once the concept of 'race' and the division between 'white' and 'black' was deployed, the trade in enslaved Africans was underpinned by an assumption of superiority of the 'pure', 'civilised', 'Christian' and 'scientific' *white* over the 'sinful', 'primitive', 'pagan' and 'irrational' *black*, providing a God-given justification in the European mind.

Looking back, albeit with a different moral emphasis and with our modern concept of human rights, the tragic irony is that the barbarism and savagery belonged to whiteness. If we are to grieve the inhuman acts of our ancestors, we are required to gaze steadfastly into the dark shadows of our white past and articulate the guilt and shame at what we find there. We have to find ways to mourn whiteness itself.

The term 'racial melancholia' is used by David Eng and Shinhee Han (2000) in their consideration of the complex situation for Asian Americans who find themselves excluded from the ideal of whiteness. Referencing their work as well as that of Straker (2004), Melanie Suchet (2007) suggests this term is also applicable to white liberals struggling with 'the loss of the ideal of whiteness as expressed in its humanitarian values of equality and justice' (p. 875). However, she points out that this loss cannot be located solely in the past: 'Not only is the ideal of whiteness betrayed, but one benefits from precisely that which contradicts one's fundamental values' (p. 874). She continues:

> The direct implication of one's privileges is difficult to absorb. The location of the hated other is now inside. It is this de-idealized self (Straker, 2004), stripped of its narcissistic accoutrements, that we must confront. . . . The melancholic state results, in part, from confronting one's racial shame – the shame of whiteness as wounder, racist and supremacist. Shame and the loss of a sense of the idealized white self is a necessary step in the undoing of whiteness.
>
> (p. 875)

As Parker's research suggests, the willingness of the modern white to acknowledge and connect imaginatively to our slaving ancestors on an individual level is limited. But, perhaps more importantly, emotional disconnection from this lineage and the disavowal of their legacy of modern-day white privilege is reflected and supported at a collective level.

In an article in the *Observer* (2015), Tim Adams interviews the American lawyer Bryan Stevenson about his fight to mark the legacy of slavery in Southern cities by having plaques put up in places where slave markets were held. However, the suggestion of erecting even small, discreet signs has met with great resistance. Apparently, there is no statue to Martin Luther King in Montgomery. Instead, his church 'is looked down upon by a lofty bronze of Jefferson Davis, last president of the confederacy, white supremacist and owner of 100 slaves'.

In Britain the trade in African slaves was made illegal in 1805, although the act abolishing slavery in the colonies wasn't passed by the British Parliament until 1833. No individual or company was brought to trial for murder or any other crime against humanity. No compensation was paid to the enslaved or to the countries from which they were taken. Instead, a total of £20 million, 40 percent of Britain's national budget at the time, was awarded to the owners of the plantations for 'loss of property'. The loan to cover this amount was finally paid off in 2015. Britain has made no apology for African slavery as it has done for the Irish potato famine, nor has it made any attempt to pay reparations to the descendants of African slaves.

In 2007 Britain celebrated the bicentenary of the Abolition of the Slave Trade Act. Whilst there was a strong and growing protest against the slave trade amongst the population, largely led by the Quaker movement, it is the politician William Wilberforce who is publicly honoured as the central representative of abolition. Identification with this hero – as opposed to those British citizens who feared for their considerable investments and who strongly opposed him – has led to a peculiar collective narrative. The centuries beforehand when Britain plied this horrific trade are not denied – the history is known, even if sparsely taught in our schools

and only vaguely understood. However, in congratulating ourselves on the abolition of the trade, and locating the responsibility for the fact that there was anything to be abolished in the first place to a few rogues and deviants on the edges of
society, we place ourselves firmly on the side of the angels. We disavow the trade,
the traders and our ancestors. This selective, myopic vision of the past led William
(Lez) Henry (2007) to describe the 2007 celebrations as a 'Wilberfarce' (p. 22).

Amazing Grace (2006), directed by Michael Apted, is a biographical-drama
film about Wilberforce and that period of British history. Kehinde Andrews (2016)
analyses the discourse underpinning the film as well as that of Amma Asante's
Belle (2013), both of which, he argues, distorts the reality and is evidence of what
he calls 'the psychosis of whiteness'. He says:

> One of the most notable features of both movies is the distinct lack of Black
> characters in either. Across both movies, there are only three Black characters
> with speaking roles; in Belle, there is the title role and a maid who has a few
> lines. In Amazing Grace Olaudah Equiano, a freed slave who wrote an infa-
> mous book about his experiences, is the only Black speaking character. And
> gives little more than a cameo experience. Both these films credit abolition to
> White agents who emancipate the passive and tortured slaves on their behalf.
>
> (p. 442)

He goes on to say:

> In these British period dramas, far removed from the savagery of slavery, Brit-
> ain is constructed as active in the fight to end the unjust slave system. Black
> agency, and even Black characters are drained from the narratives to present
> Britain and Whiteness in the role of the savior. . . . The narratives of both films
> allow the viewer to feel that slavery was wrong, but that it is in the past and
> Britain can be proud of its role, and herein lies the purpose of the psychosis.
>
> (p. 451)

Andrews describes this act of disavowal as the 'psychosis of whiteness' where

> slavery happened elsewhere and is not part of Britain's legacy, whose role in
> slavery was to abolish it, something that the whole nation should be proud
> of. Prime Minister David Cameron outlined this view when arguing against
> Scottish independence in 2015, he claimed that Britain was a nation worth
> saving because breaking it up 'would be the end of a country that launched
> the Enlightenment, that abolished slavery, that drove the industrial revolu-
> tion, that defeated fascism'.
>
> (p. 447)

Britain has a complex and unresolved relationship to its history and, in particular, its Empire. It is just over seventy years since India gained its independence

from Britain. The first African nation to gain independence, Ghana, did so in 1957. That is not a lot of time to acknowledge what the Empire meant to those we colonised and for us to adjust, to mourn and to find a different place in the world. Many argue we are not doing that well. Perhaps our collective disavowal of the power that has been lost can be found in our honour system which continues to offer awards such as the 'Order of the British Empire' to the great and the good.

The anthem 'Rule Britannia', most famously sung at the 'Last night of the Proms' at London's Royal Albert Hall each summer, is a poem by James Thomson set to music by Thomas Arne. The emphatic chorus line *Britain never, never, never shall be slaves* carries the not very subtle inference that the state of enslavement is a matter of choice, or a failure of valour, determination and resistance. By implication, all those who have been enslaved lacked such qualities and therefore were in some way responsible for their own fate. There was continual resistance by enslaved Africans throughout the history of the trade including rebellion, uprising and escape against an institutionally established system wielding far superior weaponry. The idea that any British individual faced with the same situation would have been able to refuse the state of slavery is deeply insulting.

There is now a museum of slavery in Liverpool and in 2005 the top floor of the London Docklands museum was dedicated as a museum of the slave trade in London. Bristol has nothing similar. In both Britain and the United States over the last decade or so there has been a growing concern about the statues of slavers in our towns and cities and a pressure to retitle buildings and streets which carry their names. Recently the Black Lives Matter movement has powerfully vocalised the hurt and anger caused by the monuments that were erected to those who profited directly from the trade; monuments in the form of statues, buildings, street names etc. which have been allowed to stand for centuries regardless of the hurt they caused and the message they conveyed. The argument used most often against the removal of these monuments is that it is erases history, but we need to seek knowledge and understanding of that history in our museums, school textbooks and other sources of information. A statue honours the individual and to leave them standing implies a public complicity with such a commemoration.

Britain has made no gesture of reparation for our involvement in the trade – not even a statue remembering the enslaved. To date, the charity Memorial 2007 led by Oku Ekpenyon campaigning for a memorial to slavery for some decades has had no success in getting government support. In an interview with the BBC in November 2019, Toyin Agbetu, founder of Ligali, a pan-African human rights organisation, said:

> Memorials are such an important part of the national narrative. If we've got a war memorial to animals who died [in Hyde Park], we certainly can have a memorial for some of those ancestors of many of those people in this nation who actually helped build it up.

Writing in the *Guardian* (2019), Afua Hirsch says:

But this campaign is not requesting a favour for a marginal section of society. The history of how we came to be this nation is a history for us all. If we can't dignify it with a simple memorial, one whose location, design, importance and even planning permission have already been established, then we really have lost the plot.

The word 'dignity' in the quote is key here. It was wholly absent from the attitude of the slavers and the plantation owners towards the Africans. Nor did it have any part in the attitude of those who saw the slaves as sinners deserving of their plight. Nor of the nineteenth-century anthropologists with their hierarchies and their divisions into the 'primitive' and the 'civilised'. Nor of Freud and Jung who lent so heavily on such 'armchair titans'. Those who were enslaved may be pitied or feared or disavowed but as a community, we still refuse them the respect of our grief for what has been done. Their ghosts haunt our collective calling out to be dignified after so many centuries of abusive intimacy and humiliation. If we as a society are to heal, then we must heed and respect their call.

References

Abraham, N., and Torok, M. (1994) *The Shell and the Kernel*. Vol. 1. Chicago and London: The University of Chicago Press.

Adams, T. (2015) Bryan Stevenson, 'America's Mandela'. *The Observer Newspaper*, 01.02.2015.

Andrews, K. (2016) The Psychosis of Whiteness: The Celluloid Hallucinations of Amazing Grace and Belle. *Journal of Black Studies*, 47(5), 435–453.

Bollas, C. (1987) *The Shadow of the Object. Psychoanalysis of the Unthought Known*. London: Free Association Books.

Brewster, F. (2019) *Archetypal Grief. Slavery's Legacy of Intergenerational Child Loss*. London and New York: Routledge, Taylor & Francis.

Brewster, F. (2020) *The Racial Complex. A Jungian Perspective on Culture and Race*. Oxon and New York: Routledge.

Brickman, C. (2018) *Race in Psychoanalysis. Aboriginal Populations in the Mind*. Oxon and New York: Routledge.

Chomsky, N. (1968) *Language and Mind*. New York: Harcourt, Brace, and World.

Eng, D., and Han, S. (2000) A Dialogue on Racial Melancholia. *Psychoanalytic Dialogues*, 10(4), 667–700.

Fletchman Smith, B. (2000) *Mental Slavery. Psychoanalytic Studies of Caribbean People*. London: Rebus Press.

Fletchman Smith, B. (2011) *Transcending the Legacies of Slavery. A Psychoanalytic View*. London: Karnac Books.

Frosh, S. (2013) *Hauntings: Psychoanalysis and Ghostly Transmissions*. London: Palgrave Macmillan.

Hartman, S. (2007) *Lose Your Mother. A Journey Along the Atlantic Slave Route*. New York: Farrar, Straus and Giroux.

Hazlewood, N. (2004) *The Queen's Slave Trader. John Hawkyns, Elizabeth I and the Trafficking in Human Souls*. London and New York: Harper Perennial.

Henry, W. (2007) *Whiteness Made Simple. Stepping into the Grey Zone.* London: Nu-Beyond Ltd.

Hirsch, A. (2019) Britain Was Built on the Backs of Slave. A Memorial Is the Least They Deserve. *The Guardian Newspaper*, 23.10.2019.

Kaufmann, M. (2017) *Black Tudors. The Untold Story.* London: Oneworld.

Kimbles, S. (2014) *Phantom Narratives: The Unseen Contributions of Culture to Psyche.* Lanham, MD: Rowman & Littlefield.

Miller, J.C. (2012) *The Problem of Slavery as History. A Global Approach.* New Haven, CT: Yale University Press.

Morrison, T. (2007) *Beloved.* London: Vintage (First published 1987).

Parker, R.N. (2019) Slavery in the White Psyche. *Psychoanalytic Social Work*, 26(1).

Schwab, G. (2010) *Haunting Legacies; Violent Histories and Transgenerational Trauma.* New York: Columbia University Press.

Straker, G. (2004) Race for Cover: Castrated Whiteness, Perverse Consequences. *Psychoanalytic Dialogues*, 14(4), 405–422.

Suchet, M. (2007) Unravelling Whiteness. *Psychoanalytic Dialogues*, 17(6), 867–886.

Unsworth, B. (2012) *The Quality of Mercy.* London: Windmill Books.

Walvin, J. (2007) *A Short History of Slavery.* London: Penguin.

Chapter 3

Race and racism

The origins of 'race'

Whilst prejudice, religious intolerance and antagonism between tribes, groups and nations have always existed, the division into so-called races based on skin colour, the disparagement of black and the assertion of the supremacy of white came with the colonisation of the Americas leading to a need for labour in the 'new world'. The triangular slave trade was established, bringing enslaved Africans to work the plantations for generations. Racist structures developed by the colonisers that asserted the inferiority of the black, so-called 'primitive' ensured that alliances between the poor, indentured European workers and the enslaved Africans on the basis of class were prevented. They also guaranteed support back home by church, state and the population at large for European dominion.

From its beginnings in the fifteenth century till its abolition in the nineteenth, well over ten million Africans were transported to the Americas with many dying on the way. In order to justify this highly lucrative trade, the African men, women and children who were captured and taken to the Americas to work the plantations were stripped of their humanity in the European mind. They had to be regarded as 'savage' and 'pagan' and the rich layers of civilisation and religious belief that lay deep within the African psyche had to be disregarded, vilified and ignored. Endorsed by the church, which itself profited greatly from the enterprise, the most religious of people could justify their involvement. The idea that 'there is no sin south of the equator' was a common belief endorsed by the papacy. There one could do what one wanted without fear of God's retribution. All this was designed to ensure that the enslaved Africans could be regarded as property with whom their owners could do what they wanted. Concede the African's humanity and the whole system would unravel.

It seemed to be evident to all in Europe in the sixteenth to nineteenth centuries that there were real divisions between 'races' based on fixed, immutable factors and fundamental differences within humanity, forming a natural hierarchy with black Africans at the bottom and white Europeans at the top. This led to the inevitable conclusion that it was the European's right – indeed their duty – to rule and manage those of 'lesser' breed. Religion, biology, anthropology and other sciences were used to 'prove' the reality of this belief. The roots of the need to do so lie less in the values of scientific curiosity, and more in a socio/political/economic pressure which lay behind the search for wealth and slaves in Africa, Asia and the Americas. For example, the eighteenth-century botanist Carolus Linnaeus divided humanity into four groups: Americanus, Asiaticus, Africanus and Europaeus, the divisions being based on an amalgam of physical features and behavioural traits.

As Joel Kovel (1988) puts it:

> the world is neither black nor white, but hued. A lightly-hued people – aided perhaps by fantasies derived from their skin color – came to dominate the entire world, and in the process defined themselves as white. The process that generated this white power also generated the fear and dread of the black.
>
> (p. 95)

Celia Brickman (2018) describes how the early European anthropologists of the nineteenth century sought to order and classify the data that was gathered about the non-European people of the world:

> Their theorizing was the culmination of the many attempts to order human communities according to a presumed progression from the most primitive to the most civilized according largely to skin color, attempts that had preoccupied European theorists from the sixteenth century onwards, and which fell under the sway of the mighty influence of Darwin in the late nineteenth century. But nineteenth century evolutionary theory took its cues from Herbert Spencer's interpretation of Darwin, which made use of the biological deterministic theories of Lamarck and Haeckel to explain how cultural phenomena became biologically sedimented into *racially* inherited traits.
>
> (p. 60. Italics in original)

Whilst very few of these 'armchair titans' set foot in the lands they were writing about or met any of the so-called 'primitives' they discussed, their theories were of great influence at the time – including on both Freud and Jung. According to Brickman, whilst some, referred to as polygenists, saw different races as having different origins, the influential E.B. Tyler, author of *Primitive Culture*, the 1871 book considered to be the foundational text of British anthropology, argued that all of humankind had the same rational mind and that '[d]ifferences between people and cultures merely represented different degrees of rationality, which were correlated with different stages of evolutionary development' (p. 63).

Ernst Haeckel, a German biologist, took Darwin's theory of evolution and Jean-Baptiste Lamarck's concept of acquired characteristics and developed his theory that 'ontology recapitulates phylogeny', meaning that the individual in its development repeats the history of the species. Such ideas were then combined with the ancient, still flourishing notion of The Great Chain of Being, which ranked all creation along a scale beginning with inanimate objects, moving to animals and humans, and then on to angels, and finally to God. In this Great Chain the African had been placed right after the ape.

(Ibid., p. 41)

Whilst the 'data' from which these theorists worked came from a wide variety of groups across the globe, indigenous populations in colonised territories were all regarded as 'savages', marked by a dark skin which came to signify the 'primitive', establishing the equation of the 'civilised' with white skin. Because of Haeckel's recapitulation theory, the 'dark-skinned "savages" were believed to be living in the infancy of the human race' (Ibid., p. 64). As the individual white European developed from child to adult, he or she would recapitulate the development of the species, maturing from the early 'primitive' state to that of the mature, 'civilised' European adult. This had, and continues to have, implications for psychoanalytic theory, which I discuss in a later chapter.

Modern developments

This biological essentialism has been profoundly challenged in developments in science in the last half of the twentieth century, culminating in the completion of the Human Genome Project in 2003. This project established that there is no genetic basis that corresponds with any particular group of people and now few scientists argue that there is any substantial biological basis for such classifications. All human beings share over 99 percent of their DNA and 85 percent of human genetic variation occurs within the boundaries of what are commonly labelled as racial groups, as opposed to between them.

Whilst there is genetic variation between people, mostly it is at an individual level. There is no significant essentialist DNA for black people or white people or any other grouping. Visible differences such as skin colour, eye shape and hair texture are primarily cosmetic, involving a small number of genes that were selected historically in response to certain environments. This is also considered to be the case in explaining the appearance of certain sets of genes within particular racial groups which alter the propensity of groups to be at risk from certain types of illness. For example, sickle-cell anaemia evolved in areas where malaria is common, so black British individuals whose ancestors came from West Africa may be susceptible whereas those who live in Southern Africa are not. Tay-Sachs disease, once thought to be a 'Jewish disease', is found to be as common in French Canadians and Cajuns. These diseases are the result of the historic selection of a small number of genes in response to certain environments and can be found across the so-called races.

If we now know that there is no such thing as 'race' in any way that has biological essentialist meaning, and certainly no evidence of hierarchy, then the foundations for a racist system and racism itself should collapse. The fact that this is evidently not the case implies that the underpinnings of this phenomenon are not based – indeed never have been – in any objective reality, but have their roots elsewhere.

Racism today

In his Preface to the 1988 edition of his book *White Racism*, Joel Kovel argues that 'Western civilization is saturated, not merely with racism – that is obvious enough – but with the elementary gesture out of which racism is constructed: splitting the world in the course of domination' (p. xiii). He goes on to state that:

- racism antecedes the notion of race, indeed, it generates the races;
- racism supersedes the psychology of prejudice, indeed, it creates that psychology for its own purposes;
- racism evolves historically, and may be expected to appear in different phases in different epochs and locales;
- racism cannot be legislated out of existence, since what is put into law always serves to legitimate the system which generates and is defined by it.

(pp. xiii–xiv)

'Race' is not biological, but it has a socio-political existence and an emergent rather than a natural ontology. Created by humans, it is a powerful system of social classification so the question is not what is your biological, genetic make-up, but where it is you are located, and how you are categorised within that system. For this will determine what position you are slotted into and your opportunities, expectations, life chances – your health and longevity. All these aspects will, in turn, affect your consciousness.

In Britain over the years there have been a number of attempts to legislate against racism, as well as programs for education within schools, the workplace and other settings. These are essential in preventing the most blatant, overt forms of racism but, despite all this, it seems the system remains alive and active, evidenced by the disparity in access to services, wealth and status that persists today. A major review into racial inequality in Britain was undertaken by the UK Equalities and Human Rights Commission and published in August 2016, the findings from which showed evidence of disparity across all aspects of life in Britain today. Not only were unemployment rates significantly higher for ethnic minorities compared with white people; when they are in employment blacks earned substantially less than whites, including those with degrees. Significantly lower percentages of ethnic minorities worked as managers, directors and senior officials compared with white people, and this was particularly true for African or Caribbean black people and those of mixed ethnicity.

Black women were five times more likely to die during pregnancy and child-birth than white women. Black Caribbean and mixed white/black Caribbean children had rates of permanent school exclusion – about three times that of the pupil population as a whole. Rates of prosecution and sentencing for black people were three times higher than for white people, and there was a significant disproportionate number of ethnic minorities detained under mental health legislation in hospitals in England and Wales. Members of ethnic minorities were almost twice as likely to live in poverty than white people.

I write this in the middle of the Covid-19 pandemic of 2020 where we face the shocking fact that the death rate among British black Africans and British Pakistanis from coronavirus in English hospitals is more than 2.5 times that of the white population, and the deaths of people from a black Caribbean background are 1.7 times higher than for white Britons. These statistics reflect the situation globally. Whilst the causes of this disparity will be varied and complex and further extensive research is required, evidence is already available which highlights historic and present racism in the form of disparities in living conditions and health care as a significant factor.

These are just a few all too familiar statistics which underscore the many ways people from ethnic minority communities experience the realities of discrimination within our society. It is evident that these minorities are placed within the system of racism such that they experience real disadvantage. The corollary of this is not often made explicit, that the white majority are, in turn, advantaged and thus hold a privileged position. Of course, health care, for example, should be of the highest quality for all and minority groups should receive the same level of care as the majority. On the surface this is a laudable aim, but first one needs to unpick the data to uncover any possible discrimination in the allocation of limited resources.

Other factors have more obvious implications. If, as the 2016 report states, only 8.8 percent of people from ethnic minorities 'worked as managers, directors and senior officials, compared with white people (10.7 per cent)' (p. 24), if this imbalance is to be addressed the inevitable consequence is that some of those white managers would not be in these roles. The imbalance reflects a system that produces not just disadvantage for blacks, but a system of privilege for whites.

It's a system that is embedded within and permeates the whole culture. For this result reflects not so much that black people experience discrimination at interview (although some might), but that the whole process of getting to the interview itself, through a biased educational process and the erosive undermining of self-confidence, etc. is loaded against the black individual.

We tend to locate racism in our society mainly in the act of physical or verbal abuse by one group against another. Such acts do take place and with the worrying rise of the far right, our newspapers report daily incidents of attacks on members of minority groups by white citizens. From time to time someone in the public eye says or does something regarding another group and public debate ensues, arguing the question as to whether he or she is 'racist'. Whilst any form of racist activity does immediate damage and should be challenged, by limiting our understanding of racism to just that of specific words or actions, we are free to locate the problem in others, the delineated 'racists', and we miss the wider, more pervasive point. For 'white liberals' who do not engage in such acts can detach ourselves from such groups and activities, project our internal racism into those actively racist groups and fail to see our part in the problem. Racism is a process. It has roots that go back centuries and is deeply embedded within our culture.

The negation in the last decades of the biological determinism of previous centuries reveals the concept of race as what Rustin (1991) calls an 'empty category', despite which, he argues, is also 'one of the most destructive and powerful forms of social categorization' (p. 57). The ubiquity and tenacity of racism, despite the facts, implies that it lies far deeper within the culture and within the psyche, outside of the bounded rationality of the human mind. Indeed, one might argue that it persists not *despite* the emptiness of the category of 'race', but *because* of it. A category as empty of content as this makes an ideal container for all the projections, identifications and splitting processes that are enlisted in the phenomenon of racism.

Racism in the consulting room: Dee[1]

The racist system forms a backdrop to all encounters, including those that take place in the consulting room. As an illustration of how this can impact on the clinical work, the following is an account of a particular time in my work with Dee, a woman in her early 30s whose grandparents came to the UK in the late 1950s from the Caribbean.

Dee came from a religious family where strict discipline was imposed on all the four children, of which she was the eldest. This discipline was sometimes harsh and often experienced as arbitrary, to which Dee responded by retreating into a fantasy world inside herself and away from the family. It was only in her late teens that she discovered that she had been adopted when she was six months old. Her real mother had become pregnant when still young, and her sister who had just married had taken the baby to bring up as her own. The people, therefore, whom Dee had grown up believing to be her parents were, in fact, her aunt and uncle. The birth mother left the area after which time all contact with her was lost, and the couple who adopted Dee proceeded to have three children of their own. The adoptive parents did not know the identity of the natural father.

At our initial interview I raised the fact of the colour difference between us. Dee assured me that this was not an issue, that she was used to living in a predominantly white culture and knew that she was unlikely to find a black therapist anyway. It made no difference to her. In my experience this is a common response. I know the argument that the therapist should wait for things to come up in the material and not refer to these matters unless the patient does. On the issue of difference in colour I disagree. I believe that, given power issues and possible anxiety the patient may be feeling about my response as a white person, it is a lot to expect that a black patient will risk raising the issue themselves. Stating that the difference is noticed and acknowledged by the therapist and that it can be talked about gives permission for the matter to emerge at a later date.

For some months into the therapy Dee was polite and eager to please, yet I noted that we didn't seem to really be engaged with each other. It was only after the first long break that any negativity surfaced, when she began to miss occasional sessions. This was interpreted as an expression of anger and a re-enactment of her 'disappearance' from the family as a child, but it remained a theoretical understanding and was not felt in the room by either of us. Indeed, whilst my interpretations were mostly accepted, thought about and responded to, there was a sense that we were remaining essentially at the surface and there was little real affect.

As time went on, I began to notice in me a reluctance to engage with her. Whilst I did not dread her sessions, I seemed somewhat detached and disengaged and gradually I became aware of a feeling in me in her sessions of wanting her to leave. One day, as I looked at her on the couch, the phrase 'cuckoo in the nest' came into my mind. I realised the more particular thought was that she was a 'cuckoo in *my* nest' and I didn't want her there.

Negative thoughts about analysands in the consulting room are usually accepted, welcomed even, as counter-transference responses, and helpful, therefore, in illuminating what might be going on. However, what was noticeable this time was that it was hard for me to own this experience of internal rejection of Dee as intrusive, alien and unwanted. Indeed, I was ready to 'forget' both the thought and the image that had been conjured in my mind and it took an act of active engagement to hold onto and think about it. I knew the thought and image that rejected Dee in my mind was important, but so was the further rejection of the image itself. I was ashamed of having the thought and it was this shame which was preventing my capacity to work analytically by using a negative counter-transference to further my understanding and hence my analysand's.

The best I could do was to say something along the lines that there seemed to be a wish in the room for us not to be together. Dee responded to this with some feeling of relief and began to talk of her growing sense that she didn't belong with me, that being in therapy was a betrayal of herself and maybe not right for her. Over the next few weeks, she verbally attacked therapy in a contemptuous way, describing it as tyrannical, old-fashioned and against people's thinking. Whilst she continued to attend her sessions, she spent most of the time telling me that the work was ineffectual and lacked the creative exercises and structured work she needed and often quoted texts which criticised analysis, which she seemed to seek out between sessions. In one session when she was telling me how wrong the work was for her and how she wanted to leave, she began to say how she feared that I would – and she meant to say 'brainwash' – what she actually said was that I would 'whitewash' her.

She was initially shocked by the idea that she was relating to me as a colonial, imperial power that could take her over with my mind. She was well read and understood theoretical constructs regarding transference, and she began to 'wonder' whether her fear of brainwashing was about her fear of the therapist/ mother. Her invitation to me was to interpret in terms of her internal world only. There were, indeed, thoughts about an engulfing adoptive mother who disciplined harshly, of her struggle to fit in with what is around her and only able to assert herself by leaving. I felt, however, that we needed to take care. All that was in the 'brainwashing' scenario. Something more complex was expressed in that of the 'whitewash', something we both were finding difficult to face.

Staying with the subject of colour and the difference between us, she began to express a disparagement of blackness. She said she had been relieved that I was white when she first met me because of a sense that a black therapist would be second rate and she wanted the best. She was deeply ashamed of these feelings as a woman who was politically aware and dismissive of the mimicry she saw in some black people. The self-deprecation in this was evident and illustrated how the black individual on the receiving end of white shadow projections can internalise this hostility and turn it into an attack on the self.

However, my job was to explore with her which aspects had been introjected by *her* and how this related to *her* internal world. From infancy Dee retained a sense of abandonment. She was the odd one out without understanding why. She had to be good to hold onto her mother's love, but she still kept getting beaten for crimes she did not always understand. Her general feeling throughout was of not being good enough, and her sense of belonging was extremely tenuous. Her rage at this had had no expression as a child, except in fantasies of suicide. She could only cope with the situation by imagining there was something fundamentally wrong with her.

The fact of being black in a 'white' society fitted this sense of not belonging. Her experiences of racism had provided an unconscious confirmation that she was 'bad' and deserving of punishment. Despite political alignment with the black movement, her internal sense remained that of being an outsider, of being wrong and somehow dirty. White meant belonging and white meant what she was not good, successful and of value. My whiteness meant she could get close to the source of what was good, but she had to be careful that she did not antagonise me through any exposure of her 'bad' rage.

As we explored the self-loathing inherent in her 'secret' disparagement of 'black', her comments switched from a disparagement of the blackness of herself to a disparagement of my whiteness. This was done largely through her accounts of the racism she had experienced. She seemed to be challenging me to take up a position. Was I allied with these white others or would I join with her in her attack, and become black like her? What was not to be allowed, it seemed, was our difference. I was to be for her or against her.

Whichever category was to be deemed superior to the other, the insistence that one *had* to be served to perpetuate the perception of me as 'Other'. 'Other' with a capital 'O' as, this way, I was being safely removed behind a shield of categorisation. Thus Dee could defend herself against the anxiety of her longing to become one with me and the terror of expulsion. If I rejected her it could be because she was black and bad, or because I was white and bad. The pain and frustration of me being different and separate from her could be avoided.

In his paper *Working with Racism in the Consulting Room*, Lennox Thomas (1992) describes a similar experience of a white therapist working with a black patient who was in supervision with him. Thomas says 'it is difficult for the thera-pist to recognise that the unconscious does not distinguish between colour as far as the perpetrators of pain are concerned' (p. 138). In the same paper, Thomas cites the concept, put forward by Andrew Curry (1964), distinguishing between the *pre-transference* and the *personal transference*. This, to my mind, is a useful distinction. The pre-transference is described as

> the ideas, fantasies and values ascribed to the black psychotherapist and his race which are held by the white patient long before the two meet for the first time in the consulting room. Brought up in the society which holds nega-tive views about black people, the white patient will have to work through this before engaging properly in the transference. The white psychothera-pist too will need to deal with this when working with black patients. . . . This pre-transference is constituted of material from the past: fairy tales, images, myths and jokes. Current material, in the form of media images, may serve to top up this unconscious store of negative attributes.
>
> (quoted in Thomas, 1992, p. 137)

For Dee the early loss of the mother, and the later felt tenuousness of the bond with the adoptive mother, was the pain that lay at the centre of her self. She was, in many ways, the cuckoo in the nest, not a real part of the family and not conscious of why.

The strict religious culture of this particular family meant that Dee's illegiti-macy was regarded as a sin which was covered up by the aunt's adoption of the baby. One can only speculate how the adoptive parents felt towards this child, the product of shameful intercourse, especially after the birth of their own chil-dren. Knowing what I did of this personal dynamic and its impact on her internal world, I could see that my thought, 'cuckoo in the nest' and Dee's verbal slip of the 'whitewash', needed to be understood within the personal transference. For together they told a tale of her parent's unconscious rejection of this infant, and of the child's sense of her own wrongfulness. Dee grew up not consciously know-ing that she was adopted and believed her failure to fit in was due to her 'sinful-ness'. However, she also feared that her 'rehabilitation' required a whitening that would wipe out her distinctive self. Thus, this pair of notions, one spoken (the 'whitewash') and one merely thought (the 'cuckoo'), informed a deeper under-standing of the particular vicissitudes of Dee's personal psyche, and also of the unconscious transference/counter-transference relationship between us. To that extent this is ordinary analytic work (as much as any analytic construction can be considered 'ordinary') and was clearly helpful in that Dee was visibly moved by the understanding that developed. She was able to stay in the analysis and our relationship deepened.

However, whilst clearly highly relevant to Dee's internal world, I found myself thinking further and wider about what was happening between us. For here were two individuals together in a room in North West London at the very end of the twentieth century. Both were well educated and used to the multiculturalism of a world shrunk by telecommunications and migration, and both would describe themselves as liberal in their thinking. Into this engagement two small, barely formed thoughts pushed their way forward; each unwanted, yet each managing to slip past the defences and through the cracks of the ego consciousness of the thinker.

I began to consider whether these two fears – of the cuckoo and of the whitewash – tell us anything about a larger dynamic within the social and historic framework of which Dee, a black woman, and I, a white woman, are part. I was particularly interested in the fact that we both sought initially to reject these ideas that emerged unbidden in our respective minds. We both tried to dismiss them as if they hadn't happened. It was as if they each erupted into the relationship, spoiling as they did so the benign, enlightened view we held about ourselves and about the other. Apparently, at a deeper, more raw pre-rational level, there was a fear in each of the other. The *fact* that the other was perceived as a threat was the same, but the form the threat took differed, and an amplification of these specific images may shed further light on this unconscious, asymmetrical relationship between 'black' and 'white'.

The cuckoo in the nest

The familiar phrase 'cuckoo in the nest' refers to the attribute for which the cuckoo is well known, its brood parasitism. The cuckoo does not build its own nest but lays its eggs singly in the nests of other bird species. The eggs are then incubated and reared unwittingly by the foster parents. According to the *Encyclopaedia Britannica*, various adaptations enhance the survival of the egg. These are:

> egg mimicry, in which the cuckoo egg resembles that of the host, thus minimizing rejection by the host; removal of one or more host eggs by the adult cuckoo, reducing both the competition from host nestlings and the danger of recognition by the host that an egg has been added to the nest; and nest-mate ejection, in which the young cuckoo heaves from the nest the host's eggs and nestlings.

You can't help but feel sorry for the poor host-bird. She works away building this nest for her offspring and then diligently incubates the eggs until they are ready to hatch. She is not aware that she has a foreigner, an intruder amongst her treasures. Maybe one of her own has already been tipped out to make way for this interloper. Maybe it is yet to be destroyed by this pseudo-sibling. The cuckoo is the lazy parasitic good-for-nothing penetrating the nest when the host-mother isn't looking, exploiting her efforts and her innocence.

The nest is a place of retreat, our comfortable home, the place where we belong. We 'feather our own nest' and we lay down that which we have worked for and saved, our nice little nest egg. Listen to the rhetoric in Britain today concerning immigration and one hears the fear of the bird in her nest. In this country we live with the privilege of a prosperity we hug to ourselves, fearful of the intruder who will 'steal' it from us and of the 'envious' attack of the other. The introduction of the notion of the 'bogus' as opposed to the 'genuine' asylum seeker legitimises this fear whilst at the same time allowing us to maintain a perception of ourselves as generous and hospitable to those who are deemed worthy of our acceptance. The image of the 'bogus' summons up the sham, the impostor who could exploit our 'innocence' and trick us into sharing our hard-won wealth, should we relax our vigilance. When we are not looking this intruder can contaminate the nest, usurp the rightful child and replace it with the alien. The infant's greed is an abuse of the beneficence of the mother and, as such, is sacrilege. It will gobble up our hard-earned resources whilst we flap about working to feed this impostor and looking foolish.

Put this way, the projective elements in this fear begin to emerge. If anyone has intruded into the other's nest, plundered its resources, fed off its land and displaced its children, it is the Europeans. A substantial part of the feathering of this nest has been through the exploitation of the so-called Third World. The prosperity we enjoy in the West was largely pillaged from the colonies, from slavery and exploitation, and continues via the inequality of trade today. But even deeper than this is the privilege of the white skin per se. It seems to be a great privilege indeed, and must, therefore, be guarded deep in the safe realms of the unconscious.

The whitewash

The story of white supremacy has not been told only by the whites to the whites, for it has been essential that the blacks learn the stories too and learn them well. The privilege of the white skin and the inferred inferiority of the black are messages that come through the media, through our Western institutions, through our professions. The pervasiveness of such a message gets into all of us and is one from which neither white nor black is immune. Such a message is sure to take its toll, a toll on the black individual about which Frantz Fanon (1986) writes:

> As I begin to recognize that the Negro is the symbol of sin, I catch myself hating the Negro. But then I recognize that I am a Negro. There are two ways out of this conflict. Either I ask others to pay no attention to my skin; or else I want them to be aware of it. I try then to find value for what is bad – since I unthinkingly conceded that the black man is the color of evil.
>
> (p. 197)

Fanon's book from which this quote is taken is entitled *Black Skin, White Masks*. The concept of the white mask brings us close to that of the whitewash. According to the *Chambers* dictionary this is defined as

> to cover with whitewash; to give a fair appearance to; to take steps to clear the stain from (a reputation), cover up (an official misdemeanour) or rehabilitate

(a person) in the public eye; to beat (an opponent) so decisively in a game that he or she fails to score at all.

In the therapy with Dee her unconscious slip from 'brainwash' to 'whitewash' opened up the question of her relationship to colour – both hers and mine. Dee's complex attitude clearly related to her personal story, but perhaps this also illustrates something of the dilemma of the black person in the white society. If what is perceived to be good is white, then the fairer one can become, the more one may gain acceptance. The stain, the misdemeanour, is in the blackness and so must be whitewashed, but by becoming whitened the individual is lost, as is the value of blackness. There is a wiping out, an annihilation of the diverse when a blanket of white is layered over all. In this game, the black is beaten so decisively by the whitener that 'he or she fails to score at all'.

To save oneself, a protest, a resistance is required. To stand out, to become noticed. It is the black fist in the air or the bent knee refusing the white-out.

Conclusion

Dee and I came together against a backdrop of a racist society within which we had very different histories and experiences that had played a part in structuring our internal worlds. In turn, the personal processes that were unique to our particular developmental circumstances had both utilised and been used by that racist backdrop. They were intertwined and inseparable. To analyse one and ignore the other would not only have neglected an important aspect; the resultant conclusions would have been distorted and false.

There are strong forces on both sides against the acknowledgement of the racist structures that underlie any encounter between black and white. The relationship between us built over some time included trust, insight and concern. But the fears and the aggression lay beneath and needed to emerge – as they did through the parapraxis of thought and verbal slip. Neither of us wanted them and both tried to cover them over and lose them in the general activities of a session so we could return to a relationship that relied on colour blindness. However, this would have been at the cost of a key aspect of the work and the development of insight and understanding for us both.

My fear as a white person was of the black 'Other' intruding into my privileged world, challenging my sense of entitlement and stealing my treasures. The anxiety behind this and the associated images imply an insecurity in my right to those treasures, possible guilt and awareness of my vulnerability. For just as the Europeans were dependent on their colonies or the plantation owner on his slaves, white privilege requires that there are those who are not so; they form a pairing such as Dalal (2002) describes between 'the haves and must-not-haves' (p. 122). In any such arrangement the privileged, the 'haves', fear the challenge of those without. This is partly a rational fear of an uprising or revolution, but also irrational, relating, I suspect, to guilt.

There are, it seems to me, a variety of routes the white therapist can take in our attitude to work with a black patient.

The first is to ignore the issue. This is a form of colour blindness and, in my view, a denial. A denial of difference and a denial of uncomfortable feelings this difference may invoke in both parties and in the relationship. It has the appearance of good therapeutic practice, for it seems to be seeing the individual and not the category. A consequence of this is that, should the patient bring material of racist experiences, the therapist will interpret it only in terms of the patient's internal world. A reality is not acknowledged, and an abusive situation is reinforced by the repudiation of the reality of the abuse.

The second is to acknowledge that there is an issue but it is one that exists for the black patient alone. It recognises that the patient is likely to have experienced overt racism in his or her life and that needs to be acknowledged and understood. This, I believe, still removes the problem to outside of the consulting room and can be a defence on the part of the white therapist against his or her own racist responses and therefore against shame and guilt. The responsibility for the pre-transference is left on the shoulders of the black patient.

The third is to recognise that, if I acknowledge a racist backdrop to our society, then as a white person, I too cannot be free of the phenomenon. There is an acknowledgement that racism will affect the relationship between us, and that there is a power differential inherent in that relationship over and above the power relationship which both exists and is perceived to exist between any therapist and any patient. Elaboration and exploration of the reality of this differential may provide an important means of access to the transference. My argument is that we have to manage this third position if we are to get to the place I think we need to be, that is, through to the point where the issue is not an issue.

Note

1 This example first appeared in Morgan, H. (2002) Exploring Racism. *Journal of Analytical Psychology*, 47(4), 567–581.

References

Brickman, C. (2018) *Race in Psychoanalysis. Aboriginal Populations in the Mind.* Oxon and New York: Routledge.

Curry, A. (1964) Myth, Transference and the Black Psychotherapist. *International Review of Psychoanalysis*, 45.

Dalal, F. (2002) *Race, Colour and the Process of Racialization: New Perspectives from Group Analysis, Psychoanalysis and Sociology.* Hove, East Sussex: Brunner Routledge.

Fanon, F. (1986) *Black Skin, White Masks.* London: Pluto Press (First published in 1952 by Editions de Seuil).

Kovel, J. (1988) *White Racism. A Psychohistory.* London: Free Association Books.

Morgan, H. (2002) Exploring Racism. *Journal of Analytical Psychology*, 47(4), 567–581.

Rustin, M. (1991) Psychoanalysis, Racism and Anti-racism. *The Good Society and the Inner World*. London: Verso.

Thomas, L. (1992) Racism and Psychotherapy: Working with Racism in the Consulting Room – An Analytic View. *Intercultural Therapy*. Eds: Kareem, J., and Littlewood, R. Oxford: Blackwood Scientific Publications.

UK Equalities and Human Rights Commission (2016) *Healing a Divided Britain: The Need for a Comprehensive Race Equality Strategy*. London: Equality and Human Rights Commission.

Chapter 4

The disavowal of whiteness

Janet[1]

Janet was a white woman in her late 40s who, at the time of the incident described next, had been in therapy with me for several years. She arrived at one session disturbed and shocked. Janet was a social worker in an inner-city area. She had been working with a client for some time and had become emotionally close to this young woman of 18 who she saw as vulnerable and abused. That day the client, who was also white, had told Janet that she had started a sexual relationship with a black man she had met in a club in the Brixton area of London. Janet's instant, raw reaction to this news had been one of fear and distaste, followed by a sense of shame and distress at her own 'unthinking' reaction.

Janet considered herself to be a rational, liberal person who was used to having black colleagues and friends and thought she had 'worked through' issues of racism. She recognised that her reaction was rooted in a stereotype of a black man and was ashamed of her initial response, which she considered racist. Janet reported the event and the shock of her reaction at the start of the session but hastened to assure me that she had thought it through, and things were OK now. Soon she was on to another subject and apparently the matter was over and done with.

I was struggling to work out what might be going on here. The recounting of this event had the feel of the confessional, where Janet was telling her secret 'sin' to me. It seemed that this was enough, and, with a sigh of relief, we could both move on.

In this she seemed to be appealing to my understanding as another white woman on two levels. One was a recognition of and familiarity with the stereotypes conjured up by the words 'black man' and 'Brixton', and the other was a liberalism that had no truck with such silly notions. Both expectations were accurate. The questions in my mind were: what was her immediate response about in terms of her internal world? What was she defending against in the shame and the wish to move on? What was being re-enacted in the transference?

Despite an uncomfortable feeling in the room, I returned to the subject of the client's boyfriend and the apparent avoidance of any further thinking about the matter. Struggling with feelings of shame and embarrassment, Janet began to articulate her associations more explicitly.

Until the rapid rise in house prices in the inner city, Brixton had been an area of London where the majority population was of African-Caribbean descent and for Janet it represented London's 'Heart of Darkness', a vibrant but fearful place which both repelled and fascinated her. Locating this black man in Brixton increased a sense of both excitement and dread. Janet imagined this man to be sexually active and attractive and she was able to acknowledge both her fear of him as threat and her envy of the client having this exciting sexual object. She had already imagined the man making the young woman pregnant, then abandoning her. The fear of the aggressive, contaminating and feckless phallic male was evident.

Along with some complex processes that were specific to the internal world of my patient, a few main themes emerged relevant to the subject of whiteness. One was the projection of an animal male sexuality onto the man and an innocent, pure femininity onto the client who had to be protected. But there was also her sense of 'badness' and shame at having these aggressive and penetrating thoughts. Despite her commitment to anti-racist practice, she was still capable of such 'bad' thoughts which had intruded into her mind like an aggressive attack. In themselves they were shadow aspects which penetrated, left her with a shitty baby and then abandoned her. The client, perceived as the victim of the black man, was 'innocent' and 'pure' of such nasty notions.

Despite the urge to dismiss them from her mind and forget they ever arose, these responses were sufficiently troubling for her to bring them to her therapy and speak them out loud. She understood that the initial reaction expressed an internal state that she wished, at least in part, to explore with me. However, the reporting of her subsequent thinking and the moving on to other topics suggested an invitation to conspire both with her initial disgust and with her subsequent shame. Her 'confession' followed by the response 'it's all right now' seemed to be an appeal for me to ally myself with the aggressive intruding thought, the innocent female victim and the rescuer who protected my patient from this attack by denial and silence.

This invitation to collude was tempting. I recognised both the initial response and the shame it provoked, making it all too easy and far more comfortable to let the session move on to some other subject. While these responses may have been used unconsciously by my patient to support her avoidance, they were not only counter-transference responses; for they included more general processes familiar to me as a white individual living in a white, racist society. What was going on here?

Shame, guilt and 'guiltiness'

Most analytic theoretical perspectives on how racism operates in the mind look to the processes of splitting and projection as a way of understanding how an individual might unconsciously deploy the division into the so-called races as a receptacle for the projection of the shadow aspects of the self into the 'other'. This 'other' is then depersonalised and responded to as if they held such attributes. This makes sense of Janet's initial feelings of disgust, fear and envy.

But such an understanding applies to other forms of projection, the exploration of which may well raise anxiety and be uncomfortable, but which isn't usually accompanied by the shame and anxiety that were present in the room at that moment. Or, at least, even if the analysand is worried, it isn't usually an anxiety that echoes in me.

The white liberal's sense of goodness includes a conscious rejection of the splits and projections involved in racism. The arising of any racist feeling contradicts this sense of goodness and creates such discomfort and anxiety that the thought is ignored and 'forgotten'. Disapproval of such racist thinking is carried by the individual and reflected within white liberal society and sits alongside the reality of racism and white privilege.

Julian Lousada (1997) says:

> There are, it seems to me, two primary traumas associated with racism. The first is the appalling inhumanity that is perpetrated in its name. The second is the recognition of the failure of the 'natural' caring/humanitarian instincts and of thinking to be victorious over this evil. We should not underestimate the anxiety that attends the recognition of these traumas. In its extreme form this anxiety can produce an obsequious guilt which undertakes reparation (towards the oppressed object) regardless of the price. What this recognition of a profoundly negative force fundamentally challenges is the comfort of optimism. Being able to tolerate the renunciation of this idea, and the capacity to live in the presence of our own positive and destructive thoughts and instincts is the only basis on which the commitment to change can survive without recourse to fundamentalism.
>
> (p. 41)

The development of the capacity for guilt and concern is an important stage in the child's development. It is when the infant begins to recognise that the object of their rage is also the object of their love and to tolerate the possibility that they may have hurt the other. Feelings of concern arise together with the wish to make reparation. This capacity to feel genuine guilt and care is a key feature of what is referred to as the depressive position.

However, when blocked and unconscious, guilt can bring anxiety, shame and depression. If there is no acknowledgement of the damage done, no acceptance of responsibility and therefore no act of reparation, the defences against the accompanying anxiety become mobilised. The guilt may be projected onto the other together with an assumption of a desire for retaliation, and we become fearful that we will be attacked, overcome or even wiped out by those who we have injured. When such defences are active on a collective scale, and when one group holds power over the other, then further assaults may be made on those who are deemed to be causing our troubles.

The archetypal purity, innocence and goodness that is enfolded into the uncontaminated sense of whiteness also rejects the stain of the racist thought and denies the projective processes that are involved. The arising of such a thought contradicts a sense of goodness and creates such discomfort and anxiety that the thought is ignored; indeed, it may barely reach conscious awareness. This disapproval is carried by the individual but is also reflected within white 'liberal' society – the same society which remains structured in a way which privileges whites. If white privilege *and* the affirmed non-racist position are to exist side by side, both the individual psyche and the social system have to find a mode of operation which appears to manage these two contradictory positions with the minimum of anxiety. This is where the process of disavowal comes in.

This may take the form of straightforward denial but it can also lead to what Mitchell (2000) names as 'guiltiness'. He writes, 'genuine guilt entails an acceptance of accountability for suffering we have caused others (and ourselves). Without genuine guilt, we cannot risk loving, because the terror of our destructiveness is too great', adding that '[g]uilt needs to be distinguished from what we might term "guiltiness" – perpetual payments in an internal protection racket that can never end' (p. 731).

Adrienne Harris (2012) suggests that 'guiltiness' might be thought of as guilt in the paranoid-schizoid position:

> The state of alienation and brittle, covered emptiness leaves the person bearing 'whiteness' in a double state of knowing and not knowing, depending on a polarized idea of racial identity and at the same time disavowing its falseness, its defensiveness, its empty dangers. . . . An element in this aspect of white identity, including liberal identities, is an odd, anxious hand-wringing guiltiness.
>
> (p. 203)

Elaborating on this notion of 'guilty whiteness', Harris (2012) says:

> [g]uiltiness is a kind of hysterical form of attachment and narcissism, not a break with [the] colonizing gaze or structure. It makes for ruptured, anxious, dissociated speech. Perhaps this is a reasonable first step from the seamless voice of authorized and naturalized identities, from keeping otherness in a fetishized state. But guiltiness too often includes a demand for maternal care, for forgiveness and solace.
>
> (p. 205)

This 'odd' anxiety is often present when the subject of race and racism arises among white people. It was there in the room between Janet and me, suggesting that the process of socialisation in this matter has a depth and an early, infantile history. It made me wonder how the baby who is born pink learns to become white.

Learning whiteness

Recent research, mainly in the US but also in Europe, shows that children recognise both the fact of difference and the inherent privilege in whiteness far earlier than is usually thought.

Sociologists Van Ausdale and Feagin (2001) studied 3- to 6-year-olds in an American urban nursery school using an observational research method. They found that children learnt to identify racial or ethnic markers such as skin colour and use them to gain social control, although such activities were curbed when adults were present: 'Not surprisingly, all children in this society learn at an early age that, generally speaking, whiteness is privileged and darkness is not – and thus their choices in this regard are usually not surprising' (p. 57).

Phyllis Katz (2003), then a professor at the University of Colorado, led a longitudinal study to determine when children develop racial bias, following one hundred African American children and one hundred European American children for their first six years. When the children were 3, they were shown photographs of other children and asked them to choose whom they would like to have as friends. Of the white group, 86 percent picked other white children. When they were between 5 and 6, Katz gave these children a small deck of cards with drawings of people on them. Katz asked the children to sort the cards into two piles any way they wanted. Whereas only 16 percent split the piles on the basis of gender, 68 percent did so on the basis of race.

Troyna and Hatcher (1992) studied children in predominantly white primary schools in Britain. They found that race is a significant element in the lives of black and white children – both in their social relationships and in their understanding of society. This is the case even where the black children are in a small minority. For the children they studied, race is not experienced in isolation but is interwoven with other social dynamics, nor are the processes of racialisation of attitudes and behaviour static or consistent.

In 2009 Monteiro et al. published their findings from a study of 283 white children aged between 6–7 and 9–10 who were given the task of allocating resources to white and black target children when a) the white interviewer was present and b) when they were absent. The 6- to 7-year-old children discriminated against the black children whether the adult was present or not, whereas the older group discriminated against black children only when the white adult was absent. This challenged the hypothesis that white children's expressions of prejudice do not necessarily decline due to the development of cognitive skills. Instead it seemed that the older children had taken on a socio-normative approach that prevented blatant expressions of racism that clearly persisted.

The evidence suggests that a child born into a Western society where the formulations regarding racial differences are already in place recognises racial differences and the advantages of being born with a white skin. The white child mostly sees people who look like them and their family members on TV, in films, adverts, etc. and comes to believe that 'whiteness' is the norm. In the white liberal household, they are unlikely to hear anything explicit or overt about superiority/inferiority, yet they will be taking on a sense of privilege that comes with their skin colour. They will also be learning this is not to be mentioned.

Colour blindness

Despite the fact that they only observed and recorded what occurred between children, Van Ausdale and Feagin (2001) experienced some hostility from white parents regarding their findings. They say: 'When most adults are confronted with evidence that three-year-olds are masters at managing racial-ethnic relations, they often become disturbed, try to rationalize the evidence away or dismiss our evidence as unique' (p. 159). They go on to say:

> This failure to acknowledge the importance of racial groups in children's lives arises from the twin adult convictions that children are naïve and that colour blindness is not only desirable but achievable. . . . Frankly put, many white adults insist that racial distinctions do not matter, while all around them children see ample and compelling evidence that they do matter, and matter very much indeed. One practical response to this ideological contradiction by white children is to conceal the creation of their own racial understandings and relationships, at least while the prying eyes of adults are on them. This enables them to reproduce the racial-ethnic hierarchy in their own relationships without interference from adults.
>
> (pp. 190–191)

Children are curious creatures who seek to establish the social dynamics and systems implicit in the society into which they are born. As they begin to experience a social environment that they see discriminating on the basis of visible features, they are likely to make occasional comments and ask questions about this very real situation they are observing. Some may concern matters of fact ('Mummy, why is that man brown?') and some may relate to the structure of racism they are beginning to experience and play a part in (such as in the example of Renee and Lingmai given later).

The white adults around them, lacking the racial resilience DiAngelo (2018) speaks of, are too often unable to address directly the child's concerns regarding the privileges of their white skin. The child needs help to think about what they observe about the racist structures of society and to connect their inherited privilege with a developing concern for fairness. They need a language for thought from which effective action can develop. However, many white adults become embarrassed, hush the child, ignore or distract them, or resort to the short-cut of colour blindness by insisting that everyone is the same and equal. Such an assertion is not only untrue and denies what the child has observed and experienced. By focusing on the universality of humans, the message is conveyed that it is the *recognition* of difference that is the cause of racism, rather than the fact that the child has been born into a social system that discriminates against certain groups which they need help to acknowledge, understand and begin to think through how they might respond.

The white child trying to make sense of her or his experience and observations effectively meets silence, denial and avoidance and so he or she soon learns that ordinary curiosity regarding this specific topic is unwelcome and unwanted. When children see their parents and other adults tense up when they are with people from minority ethnic groups, or they notice that their parents' friends and contacts are not very diverse, or witness the impacts of subtle forms of racism, they will understand that the colour of one's skin *does* matter, but in a secret way. As Katz (1976) points out:

> Children who develop in this way are robbed of opportunities for emotional and intellectual growth, stunted in the basic development of the self, so that they cannot experience or accept humanity. This is a personality outcome in which it is quite possible to build into children a great feeling and compassion for animals and an unconscious fear and rejection of differing human beings. Such persons are by no means prepared to live and move with either appreciation or effectiveness in today's world.
>
> (pp. 13–14)

Black parents will be far more alert to the fact of racism and the dominance of whiteness in the society in which their children are growing up and will have to respond to and reframe their children's experiences. In 2007, a study of 17,000 American families with preschool children found that non-white parents are about three times more likely to discuss race with their children than white parents, 75 percent of whom never, or almost never, talk about race. White parents may feel they don't have to engage with the subject and, indeed, may feel uncomfortable in doing so. Both the confidence and sense of entitlement that comes with inhabiting a world which reflects you and your life, as well as a contract of silence about the disparities, is passed on from parent to child.

Lawrence Hirschfeld (2012) has conducted a number of research projects exploring the development of race awareness in children, and from these and the results of other similar studies he challenges what he sees as the 'seven myths of race and the young child'. These are:

- The colour-blind myth (Part 1): young children are by nature innocent of race.
- The colour-blind myth (Part 2): even if they are 'aware' of race, they are without prejudice.
- The perceptual myth: children 'discover' race by opening their eyes and looking.
- The parent myth: children may come to notice race on their own, but have to be taught prejudice.

- The skin-deep myth: children notice race, they may even acquire a form of racial bias, but ultimately they believe that race is a superficial quality, literally just skin-deep.
- The as-the-child-acts myth: if a child acts colour blind, he is.
- The multicultural myth: reducing prejudice is best achieved by affirming that deep down everyone is the same and/or that any difference between them should be celebrated, not scorned.

Systematically confronting each of the myths, Hirschfeld argues that:

> an extensive literature, relying on a range of methodologies, converges on the same conclusion: beginning around three and largely systematized by five years of age, children come to hold attitudes that reflect the prevailing racial prejudices that favor the majority and disfavor the minorities.
>
> (p. 21)

The common understanding of how children develop race awareness is that it is a 'bottom-up' process whereby the child notices physical differences between themselves and others, then hears derogatory comments about those who have a darker skin. Hirschfeld confronts this perception positing instead that the process is more one that is 'top-down'. He says:

> The young child does not learn about race in isolation but learns about race in the more global task of parsing the social world. This consists of attending to information that is relevant to the scope of the social groups that exist in the world.
>
> (p. 30)

He goes on to say:

> Given all this, it makes sense that young children adopt a top-down approach to acquiring information about the prevailing social ontology, relying on a learning strategy that focuses attention on the logic of the system rather than worrying the details of individual identification A child acquiring knowledge of race is in the business of acquiring knowledge of the kinds of things of which society is composed, not a catalogue of corporal variation.
>
> (p. 31)

Thus, the child comes to learn that 'white' is the preferred and privileged category and 'black' is not, without necessarily being clear about what physical characteristics are pertinent to either category.

Disavowal

The following is an example from Van Ausdale and Feagin's (2001) observational study in an American day care centre. In this instance Renee (4, white) is pulling Lingmai (3, Asian) and Jocelyn (4.5, white) across the playground in a wagon:

> Renee tugs away enthusiastically, but the task is difficult. Pulling this heavy load across loose dirt is more than Renee can handle. Suddenly she drops the handle, which falls to the ground, and stands still, breathing heavily. Lingmai, eager to continue this game, jumps from the wagon and picks up the handle. As Lingmai begins to pull, Renee admonishes her, 'No, no. You can't pull this wagon. Only white Americans can pull this wagon'. Renee has her hands on her hips and frowns at Lingmai. The Asian girl tries again to lift the handle of the wagon, and Renee again insists that only 'white Americans' are permitted to do this task. This is the breaking point and adult intervention is now sought.
>
> Lingmai sobs loudly and runs to a nearby teacher, complaining that 'Renee hurt my feelings'. . . . [W]e see the child's discretion at work. She offers no more than hurt feelings to explain her actions to the teacher. Since intervention is in order, the teacher approaches Renee. 'Did you hurt Lingmai's feelings?' the teacher asks Renee, who glumly nods assent. This is a familiar ritual. 'I think you should apologize', the teacher continues, 'because we are all friends here, and friends don't hurt each other's feelings'. "Sorry', mutters Renee, not looking at Lingmai, 'I didn't do it on purpose'. Lingmai stands silently. The teacher waits for a few moments, then finishes with, 'OK, can you guys be good friends now?' Both girls nod without looking each other and quickly move away. The teacher stands and waits for a moment or two, to assure herself that the conflict does not erupt again, then moves off.
>
> (p. 104)

Both Renee and Lingmai have already worked out that racial identity and colour have powerful implications in social relations, and both recognise that Renee's words and actions are hurtful. However, both also seem to realise that the factor of race needs to be kept away from any involvement of an adult. Lingmai did not reveal to the teacher that race was involved in the dispute, even though that would have got Renee into a lot more trouble and, in one sense, Lingmai would have triumphed. But she may well have enough experience of how 'white American' power operates to know that a temporary gain might not be worth longer-term punishment. Thus, whilst Renee has to apologise, her position is not challenged – and, indeed, is confirmed for them both.

The 4-year-old Renee has already grasped that there are groups within society who have power and privilege, and there are those do not. She may not understand what the concepts 'white' and 'American' mean, but she does recognise that they can be used to exclude:

> She is incorporating whiteness as part of her identity and knows that this identity gives her power over the racial other. And, most important, she acts on her understandings. . . . The critical issue of group membership figures strongly in this incident.
>
> (p. 105)

Renee has also learnt that this knowledge had to be kept secret from adults. When one knows something and yet all the messages from important adults are that it shouldn't be known, the psyche has to repudiate some or all of the meaning of reality. Internally, two conflicting situations develop and, in order that they can coexist, a vertical split is created within the psyche. This split is reflected in, and reinforced by, the wider social system, allowing both the reality of white privilege and its disavowal.

A 'psychose blanche'?

In psychoanalytic theory, an internal conflict between superego, ego and id may lead to the creation of *horizontal* splits in the psyche where aspects of the self are repressed, made unconscious and denied. Outside of conscious awareness, these repressed elements of the psyche can have a damaging and conflictual impact on the individual's life and relationships. In order to ameliorate anxiety, unwanted, rejected aspects of the self may be projected into others and feared, idealised or hated, and the difficult work of what Lousada (1997) describes as 'the capacity to live in the presence of our own positive and destructive thoughts and instincts' (p. 41) may be avoided through splitting between extremes of good and bad, love and hate. These repressed elements may make themselves known through parapraxes such as slips of the tongue or pen, forgetfulness, misplacement of objects, or in the images of dreams. In analytic work, moments of enactment within the transference often allow access to hidden, unconscious dynamics which are made available for interpretation and understanding, offering the potential for integration within the conscious psyche.

Whilst also a defensive process, disavowal develops *within* the ego when it is faced with two conflicting realities, causing a *vertical* split within the psyche. Unlike repression, the individual remains conscious of both sides of the split but will disavow either to meet internal desires and needs or minimise anxiety. Thus, I can know the reality of the consequences of my behaviour but will disregard that awareness in order to satisfy my desires, my omnipotence and my narcissistic sense of entitlement. Disavowal features strongly in addiction, where the person is fully aware of the consequences of continuing their behaviour; an awareness that will be put aside and ignored in the service of meeting the need for the drug of choice. It can be seen operating collectively and in individuals in relation to the climate emergency.

The child growing up in a white liberal family comes to recognise that they are white and that there are black 'others' not so privileged. They are socialised into a world of white solipsism where, apart from the occasional exception, it is whites who are given the significant and interesting roles, whilst blacks are more often relegated to those of service, sport, music or crime.

However, they are also being acculturated into the liberal narrative which, exacerbated perhaps by the 'purity' that is embedded in the very notion of whiteness, abjures the realities of racism. Thus, the white individual – and the white collective – has to maintain *both* white privilege *and* an acceptable perception of the self. The privileged position is rooted in deep racist social structures, and hence a self-serving attachment to the benefits of whiteness brings with it the splits and projections of racism. Racist thoughts will arise in the individual's mind. However, such thoughts, words or acts threaten the sense of oneself as a 'good' person. This will be partly a matter of persona, how one wants to seem to be, but will also include genuine interconnected concern for others. As with Janet, the tension between these two positions is 'solved' by disavowal.

I suggest this vertical split as it relates to racism is not merely a single line dividing two parts of the psyche, with the investment in white privilege and the racist thought on one side, and the condemnation and rejection of racism in the other. On both sides there remains a capacity for symbolisation which is lacking in certain moments when we are reminded of our racism. The internal psychic structure can be imagined as made up of two vertical layers between which there is a gap, a silent, empty place devoid of symbols in which it is impossible to play or grieve.

Adrienne Harris (2012) states:

> It may be that there is in 'whiteness' a 'psychose blanche' named by Andre Green (1970) for quite other purposes. Deeper than depression, deeper than rage, there is a blankness, a place where there is not sufficient structure for mourning, where the psyche gives way. Perhaps this is what 'whiteness' is: the disruption or erasure of mourning, a gap in the psyche, which through 'whiteness' functions like an imploding star, refusing signification. It is not trauma solely that is whitened out but also destructiveness and memory.
>
> (p. 207)

Green's concept, 'psychose blanche', refers to a hole in the psyche created by the child's experience of the *dead mother*. As Green points out, this does not relate to the situation where the mother[2] has actually died, but one where her previously lively engagement with the child is interrupted following an experience of loss – such as through a bereavement or a miscarriage. The term 'blanche' in French can mean either 'white' or 'blank' and Green uses it to refer to a problem of emptiness, or a negative that follows a decathexis of the maternal object. Mourning cannot take place, nor can the loss be symbolised.

I recognise that Green is referring to a stage of infancy which is primary and prior to what Winnicott would describe as that of integration, but I think it's worth considering whether such a notion has some applicability when thinking about the development of whiteness in the child.

In most other aspects of her or his life, the white child in a modern liberal family can take their curiosity regarding the social milieu they seek to understand and to find their place within to the significant adults in their life. For the majority of the time their experience will be of lively engagement, attention and interest. When they raise the matter of differences concerning race and ethnicity and they are responded to with the sterility of a blanket colour-blind position, the lively, engaged presence they had known previously disappears, and they are faced with a blankness, a shutting down and a silencing. There is a 'deadness' which relates to the subject and the child quickly learns that the topic is not welcome for discussion. Their curiosity and developing concern for others, their preoccupation with the troubled matter of social fairness, is shut down and the vertical split of disavowal develops within the psyche.

Ryan Parker (2019) writes:

> A critical component of these processes of disavowal are the ways that white children learn to disconnect – to stop thinking, to stop noticing, to stop linking reality and history, and to turn off their empathic curiosity and care. If allowed to develop this curiosity and care would cause problems for whiteness' power and the privileges it claims and protects, for it would result in recognition of reality, which eventually might lead to responsibility-taking and reparation. . . . In addition to being effectively silenced, the parental message is clear: you will get no help from me with this, nor will you get my love and approval if you pursue your curiosity and insist on maintaining conscious contact with these disavowed realities of racism and violence that are inside and everywhere around us.
>
> (p. 8)

I recall that when I was a child, jokes about Jews circulated among the children from time to time. I don't know how much I or my friends understood them, but they formed part of the currency in negotiating inclusion and exclusion in the playground. I don't recall any adult telling such a joke and yet we could only have discovered them from within the social collective we were struggling to understand. I do remember it being clear that the stories would be disapproved of, so they were never to be mentioned to parents or teachers. The jokes themselves may have expressed something around resources and withholding, and involved a projection of neediness, greed and hostility, but my sense is that it was the racism within them that was exciting and taboo. But I imagine such thoughts were also troubling. The empathic curiosity and concern I might have felt towards theses designated 'others' had no outlet either amongst our giggling friends or with trusted adults and we were left with a void, a silent space between two conflicting perceptions of the world and our place within it.

In the dead space of the gap symbolisation is suspended and so, therefore, are play and mourning. Instead the hole is patched over. The colour-blind position, the assertion that 'we are all equal, we are all the same', is a fantasy created to erase disagreeable and unwelcome facts – a fantasy which serves to perpetuate the racism and the privilege it purports to deny.

Janet

Writing more generally about vertical splits, Arnold Goldberg develops Kohut's formulation of the process of disavowal in 'Being of Two Minds: The Vertical Split in Psychoanalysis and Psychotherapy' (2000). In his review of Goldberg's book, Sigmund Katerud (2000) summarises the dynamic when this split makes an appearance in the consulting room:

> When a person enters the patient role the same scenario will be created in the transference. There is an unconscious expectation that the therapist will condemn split-off parts (e.g. misbehavior) yet at the same time engage in a silent conspiracy of not taking them seriously enough to talk about.
>
> (p. 258)

When Janet related the incident with her client and her initial racist responses, her 'misbehaviour', she did so with no sense of justification or excuse – these thoughts were regarded as 'racist' and 'wrong' and, as such, I was expected to join with her in condemning them. However, the invitation to conspire with her, to not take them seriously enough to talk about them, to bury them without mourning, repeated a process that I suspect began when she was young.

The challenge to the therapist when faced with vertical forms of splitting is always considerable, for the work of integration requires movement both vertically to unconscious material and horizontally across the disavowed aspects. However, it is especially difficult when there is a split in the therapist that matches that of the patient. There is no reason to believe that I, as a white woman raised in a white racist society with liberal parents, experienced anything fundamentally different in my early years regarding race than Janet had. Both the unconscious acceptance of racism and its condemnation created the same vertical split within me. I had no trouble understanding both Janet's original thoughts and their rejection, as well as the seeking of the confessional and the absolving of the sin via a conspiracy of silence.

But the liberal position is complex and entangled. If the mechanism of denial was complete, Janet may have entirely ignored or 'forgotten' her initial reactions and they would not have been mentioned. Part of the motivation for doing so may be seen as a way of seeking absolution through my identificatory silence, but she was also genuinely troubled by her initial reaction and was open to working with me to explore it further. Whilst the disavowal mechanism has early roots, it exists alongside an honest concern for the other, as well as a commitment to fairness, equality and human rights – all central features of liberalism. The child may learn and incorporate the dead response she meets, but it is a loss and the lack will be felt. 'Guiltiness' cohabits alongside healthy, appropriate remorse with its desire to make reparation, and they both need recognition.

The mechanism of disavowal is often so efficient and swift that thoughts that betray internal racist structures may hardly be noticed and rapidly forgotten. Attention is needed to catch them as they arise so they can become available for study. Janet's responses had been sufficiently strong and troubling to stay with her and to tell me, but effort on both our parts was needed to return to them. The deadness, the anxious silence of the gap in the structure of disavowal, refuses symbolisation, making analytic work impossible from that place. But we *could* elaborate the defences on either side of the gap where free association and imagination remained viable, so that we were gradually able to talk about the silent, dead space from a place of life.

Notes

1 This example first appeared in Morgan, H. (2014) Between Fear and Blindness. *Thinking Space. Promoting Thinking About Race, Culture, and Diversity in Psychotherapy and Beyond*. Ed: Lowe, F. London: Karnac.
2 I am using the term 'mother' to refer to the primary carer, who may or may not be the biological 'mother'.

References

DiAngelo, R. (2018) *White Fragility. Why It's So Hard for White People to Talk About Racism*. New York: Beacon Press.

Goldberg, A. (1999) *Being in Two Minds: The Vertical Split in Psychoanalysis and Psychotherapy*. Hillsdale, NJ: The Analytic Press.

Green, A. (1970) The Dead Mother. *On Private Madness*. London: Hogarth Press.

Harris, A. (2012) The House of Difference, or White Silence. *Studies in Gender and Sexuality*, 13(3), 197–216.

Hirschfeld, L.A. (2012) Seven Myths of Race and the Young Child. *Du Bois Review*, 9(1), 17–39.

Katerud, S. (2000, Fall) Review of 'Being in Two Minds': The Vertical Split in Psychoanalysis and Psychotherapy. *Journal of Psychotherapy Practice and Research*, 9(4), 257–258.

Katz, P. (1976) *Toward the Elimination of Racism*. New York, Toronto, and Oxford: Pergamon Press.

Katz, P. (2003) Racists or Tolerant Multiculturalists? How Do they Begin? *American Psychologist*, 58(11), 897–909.

Lousada, J. (1997) The Hidden History of an Idea: The Difficulties of Adopting Antiracism. *Integrity and Change, Mental Health in the Market Place*. Ed: Smith, E., 34–48. London: Routledge.

Mitchell, S.A. (2000) You've Got to Suffer If You Want to Sing the Blues: Psychoanalytic Reflections on Guilt and Self-Pity. *Psychoanalytic Dialogues*, 10(5), 713–733.

Monteiro, M., de Franca, D.X., and Rodrigues, R. (2009) The Development of Intergroup Bias in Childhood: How Social Norms Can Shape Children's Racial Behaviours. *International Journal of Psychology*, 44(1), 29–39.

Morgan, H. (2014) Between Fear and Blindness. *Thinking Space. Promoting Thinking About Race, Culture, and Diversity in Psychotherapy and Beyond.* Ed: Lowe, F. London: Karnac.

Parker, R.N. (2019) Slavery in the White Psyche. *Psychoanalytic Social Work*, 26, 1.

Troyna, B., and Hatcher, R. (1992) *Racism in Children's Lives: A Study of Mainly White Primary Schools.* New York: Routledge.

Van Ausdale, D., and Feagin, J. (2001) *The First R: How Children Learn Race and Racism.* Lanham, MD: Rowman & Littlefield.

Chapter 5

Freud and Jung

Born at the end of the nineteenth century when Europe dominated much of the world and the trade in African slaves had not long been abolished, psychoanalysis, with its key concepts of the unconscious, the id, infantile sexuality, etc. placed the 'Heart of Darkness' deep within the psyche of all humans, including the coloniser. In so doing Freud potentially challenged the accepted division between the 'civilised' white European and the so-called 'primitive' indigenous populations. On the one hand, by demonstrating the tenuousness of the power of the rational ego, it subverts the European Enlightenment view with its emphasis on science, rationality and control. Such a view legitimised binary, oppositional thinking which became incorporated into the structuring of the social and political system, heralding an alienation from the natural world.

On the other hand, as Hillman (1986) points out:

> The convention informing geographical discoveries and the expansion of white consciousness over Africa continues to inform psychic geography. The topological language used by Freud for 'the unconscious' as a place below, different, timeless, primordial, libidinal and separated from consciousness, recapitulates what white reporters centuries earlier said about West Africa. . . . Part of psychology's myth is that the unconscious was 'discovered' as its contents are 'explored'. Even the notion of the underworld as black rather that grayish, misty or invisible bespeaks white supremacy.
>
> Moreover, the 'discovery' of an unconscious separate from consciousness, as a black continent separated from white penetration into it, maintains the very unconsciousness within white which the idea was invented to wound.
>
> (pp. 45–46)

The 'primitive'

Both Freud and Jung relied heavily on the early anthropologists, the so-called armchair titans of the nineteenth century, such as Taylor, Haeckel and Lamarck. Taking their theories of human hierarchies, the inheritability of acquired characteristics, the assumption of European 'civilisation' and the 'barbarism' of the colonised, as well as Haeckel's theory that 'ontology recapitulates phylogeny', both men regarded the black 'primitive' as representing

- the early stages of the development of the European,
- the 'uncivilised', unrepressed id contents of the Western psyche, and
- the mind of the European infant.

> There are men still living who, as we believe stand very near to primitive man, far nearer than we do, and whom we therefore regard as his direct heirs and representatives. Such is our view of those whom we describe as savages or half-savages, and their mental life must have a particular interest for us if we are right in seeing in it a well-preserved picture of an early stage of our own development.
>
> (Freud, 1913, p. 53)

The adoption of these ideas by Freud and Jung was not inevitable. In the early part of the twentieth century there were those who criticised this way of thinking and offered alternative constructions. For example, as Andrew Samuels points out, Franz Boas, considered the father of American anthropology, was well known at the start of the century. Referencing Sonu Shamdasani (2003, pp. 277–278), Samuels (2018) writes:

> In his paper at the Clark University conference of 1909, with both Jung and Freud in attendance, Boas made it clear that there was no 'justification for (racial) hierarchies'. He also spoke against the idea that European civilisation represented the peak towards which other races and cultures were developing.
>
> (p. 6)

Jung also knew the anthropologist Paul Radin, who was highly critical of what he wrote about Africans.

The problematic evolutionary theories of nineteenth-century anthropology are most apparent in Freud's 1913 work *Totem and Taboo* – a treatise which has since been heavily criticised by modern day anthropologists for its ethnocentrism. Celia Brickman (2018) notes that within the psychoanalytic profession itself,

> [c]oncern with Freud's use of evolutionary theory, where there has been any, has most often been confined to the 'antiquated' and/or unsubstantiated nature of these elements of Freud's arguments rather than the graver issues of their racist implications. To assess *Totem and Taboo* as peripheral to the main concerns of psychoanalysis is to avoid reckoning with its foundational status as the origin myth of psychoanalysis and the resultant paradigmatic status of its narrative for Freud's work as a whole; and it is thus to avoid reckoning with the implications of the racial assumptions of *Totem and Taboo* for all of psychoanalysis.
>
> (p. 79)

Implications

Both Freud and Jung were speaking at a particular point in history within a certain cultural and social context and from linguistic assumptions that have changed. However, the term 'primitive' continues to be used widely within the psychoanalytic discourse without any exploration of its roots, the possible racist implications for our thinking today and the impact on black people reading such material. Whilst the term is etymologically neutral, its colonial pedigree means it carries troubling connotations. I recall no point in my training or in all the years attending clinical and theoretical seminars that anyone – including myself – raised any concerns about its historic undertones. In a recent discussion with colleagues we discovered there were a variety of perspectives on the meaning of the word, including 'original', 'primal', 'instinctive', 'regressed', 'violent', even 'unconscious'.

It will not do to dismiss the implications of such a word that appears so frequently and with such authority in the writings of our founding fathers, both of whom were fully aware of its connections to non-European peoples and the colonial attitudes of their time. Their use of the term was intended to carry a comparative imagery for the better understanding of the European individual. This forms an important part of what we as post-Freudians and post-Jungians have inherited. Given the propensity for racist thinking in the white liberal mind, to continue to use the term without proper thought means we risk perpetuating what at least consciously we now see as the error of their ways. Stephen Frosh (2017) writes:

> Under the conditions that prevailed in these great moments of formation of seminal psychoanalytic theories – and that still exert significant influence today – the idea of primitive thinking slips easily into the figure of the primitive, who by virtue of precisely this primitivity (irrationality, impulsivity etc.) becomes other to the civilized.
>
> (p. 43)

Referring to the primitive-civilised binary, Frosh goes on to say 'the point is that psychoanalysis carries over the traces of this binary as it moves into this postcolonial era. Unconsciously, it reproduces them even when used in the decolonizing movement' (p. 44).

Warren Colman (2016) has a similar warning:

> While no psychoanalyst today would associate themselves with the idea of the primitive as a racial or cultural notion, it remains deeply embedded in psychoanalytic thought and, in this way, is likely to subtly entrench out-of-awareness racist attitudes amongst the psychoanalytic community. Perhaps this is one of the reasons why our record on diversity is so poor.
>
> (p. 205)

It was in the process of exploring further the matter of whiteness and racism that led me to read texts written by psycho-social studies academics on psychoanalytic thinking from a postcolonial perspective. They offer a sympathetic, but critical, revision of many of the concepts we use. They are our profession's critical friends – or at least they would be, if we allowed their thinking to penetrate the rather limited, inward looking conversation we have with ourselves in our conferences and our journals. What I read was refreshing and challenging, provoking as it did often uncomfortable questions about my own suppositions.

Psychotherapist and academic Celia Brickman's (2018) book *Race in Psychoanalysis: Aboriginal Populations in the Mind* challenges many preconceptions and long-held assumptions. In her Introduction she describes the path that led her to writing the book, which captures something of the contradiction I found myself facing as I read further on the subject. Brickman pursued graduate studies in the humanities and social sciences where the postcolonial theorists she was reading

> considered the idea of the primitive to be a long abandoned relic of anthropology's colonialist and racist ancestry, where its evocation of the presumed inferiority of non-white and non-western peoples had contributed to the legitimation of Europe's colonial and slaving enterprises around the globe.
>
> (p. 1)

She was undertaking a clinical training in psychoanalytic psychotherapy at the same time and was struck by how often the word 'primitive' was used without questioning:

> At first, I accepted it at face value: after all, psychoanalytic theory tells us that our patterns of behavior and the roots of our pathologies lie in the earliest experiences of our lives, when our mental organization and abilities are at their most rudimentary. Why not call this level of organization primitive? Why not describe certain behaviors understood to be immature and childish as primitive? Surely the term primitive is commonly used in everyday life, not only within psychoanalytic theory to convey the raw and the rudimentary, the undeveloped, the archaic. . . .
>
>   But this psychoanalytic usage continued to bother me because it seemed remarkably indifferent to the postcolonial critique which I found so urgently persuasive. Just what did this clinical usage imply? . . . how could the clinical usage of the term primitive not be connected with the racist category which, for centuries, had classified the non-white, non-western world as eligible for colonization and domination by the west?
>
>   It finally dawned on me that what I was witnessing in these casual and not-so-casual remarks were unacknowledged traces of the racially inflected anthropological theory that had provided Freud with the foundational premises of his social thought.
>
> (pp. 1–2)

Jung

The psychiatrist and political philosopher from the French colony of Martinique, Frantz Fanon (1986), turned to Jung in his search for an understanding of the human psyche to which he could relate. But, as he says:

> Continuing to take stock of reality, endeavouring to ascertain the instant of symbolic crystallization, I very naturally found myself on the threshold of Jungian psychology. European civilization is characterized by the presence, at the heart of what Jung calls the collective unconscious, of an archetype: an expression of the bad instincts, of the darkness inherent in every ego, of the uncivilized savage, the Negro who slumbers in every white man. And Jung claims to have found in uncivilized peoples the same psychic structure that his diagram portrays. Personally, I think that Jung has deceived himself.
>
> (p. 187)

Jung believed that, in becoming 'civilised', European culture lost something important:

> Through scientific understanding, our world has become dehumanized. Man feels himself isolated in the cosmos. He is no longer involved in nature and has lost his emotional participation in natural events, which hitherto had a symbolic meaning for him. . . . He no longer has a bush-soul identifying him with a wild animal. His immediate communication with nature is gone forever, and the emotional energy it generated has sunk into the unconscious.
>
> (1948, CW 18, para. 585)

Supposing that this 'bush-soul' was to be found in the 'primitive' lands of other, 'un-civilised' continents, Jung made a number of visits abroad, including to India, the Middle East and twice to Africa. He was also interested in Native America and the impact of 'Negros' in the US.

Jung's equation between the 'primitive' black other and the European repressed unconscious led to his fear that the 'civilised' consciousness of the ego was always at risk of being overwhelmed by the 'savage'. This, he believed, was a particular danger where white Europeans mixed with black Africans, such as in colonised Africa and the United States:

> What is more contagious than to live side by side with a rather primitive people? Go to Africa and see what happens. When it is so obvious that you stumble over it, you call it going black. . . . It is much easier for us Europeans to be a trifle immoral, or at least a bit lax, because we do not have to maintain the moral standard against the heavy pull of primitive life. The inferior man has a tremendous pull because he fascinates the inferior layers of our psyche, which has lived through untold ages of similar conditions. . . . He reminds

us – or not so much our conscious as our unconscious mind – not only of childhood but of prehistory, which would take us back not more than about twelve hundred years so far as the Germanic races are concerned.

(1939, CW 10, para. 962)

The Jungian analyst Michael Vannoy Adams (1996) offers a persuasive critique of the racism in Jung's writing and suggests alternative explanations to Jung's interpretations and assumptions, especially where he considers Jung mistook what relates to his personal unconscious for something archetypal and collective. For example, he reinterprets Jung's experience of a *n'goma* (drum/dance) during a 1925 visit to the Elgonyi of Central Africa (described in Jung, 1963, pp. 270–272). At the height of the dance Jung fears it will get dangerously out of hand, so shouts and flourishes a whip in order to bring it to an end. Adams argues that Jung suffered a panic attack, equivalent to what Jung describes in another context as a 'bush fear' – a fear he associates with the collective unconscious. For Adams, what happened 'epitomizes the fear of the white European that to go black is to go primitive, to go instinctive, which is to go insane, which is to lose his ego – and, Jung says, to forfeit his authority' (1996, p. 76). Adams suggests the concept of a multicultural imagination which recognises that images of collective experiences arise as much from cultural factors – which he refers to as stereotypes – as they do from archetypal factors.

In her exploration of the relationship between analytical psychology and African Americans, Jungian analyst Fanny Brewster (2013, 2017), whilst arguing for the value of many of Jung's ideas, confronts the racist shadow in his thinking. She highlights the dubious nature of Jung's research method when he uses the dreams of fifteen African Americans at St Elizabeth's Hospital in Washington, DC, to establish the idea of the universality of the collective unconscious whilst failing to take any account of the personal or cultural associations of the dreamers or of his own European cultural bias. The image provided by one dreamer was that of a man being crucified on a wheel, which Jung linked to the Greek myth of Ixion. The 'fact' of the dreamer being a 'very uneducated Negro from the South and not particularly intelligent' (1935, CW 18, para. 81) who could not have known of the myth of Ixion was taken as crucial evidence of the non-racial, and therefore collective, nature of the archetypal image.

Despite his own assertions that the analysis of dreams requires a careful consideration of the personal aspects of the dreamer and their associations to the dream images, despite his stating that the objective psyche can only be known by detailed examination of the context within which the image emerges, it seems that here Jung was shockingly remiss in his research methodology. Neither the name nor any personal details regarding the background of this particular dreamer were recorded. Only the motif of the burning wheel is mentioned, asserting as Jung did in his 1935 Tavistock lecture that the rest of the dream was irrelevant. The association with Ixion was Jung's and not the dreamer's; indeed, it seems there is no evidence at all of any enquiry into whether this individual had his own associations to the dream image.

As Brewster points out, such associations, together with a deeper understanding of the cultural and historical context of all African Americans, would have produced a more complex picture. The history of slavery in the United States included lynchings, which frequently involved burning wheels – a motif of which the dreamer would have been aware. She also notes that, even if we were to link the dream to the myth of Ixion, the myth is itself a complex one with a number of motifs. One central theme is that of kinship and betrayal, which she convincingly argues are themes relevant to the history of slavery in the US. Such an amplification along the lines of Jung's own proclaimed method might have led to an opening of a far more intricate, more interesting interpretation of the dream – an interpretation which would include both a racial and cultural layer to the understanding of the dream, but also one which might have foregrounded a more positive reading of African American culture than the negative, potentially contaminating perspective that Jung seemed to hold. The fact that Jung used this 'evidence' to assert the non-racial aspect of the collective unconscious and, therefore, its universality is troubling.

In his paper 'Jung: A Racist', Dalal (1988) highlights the racist nature of Jung's thinking when theorising about non-Europeans, listing a number of quotes from his writing which are disturbing to the modern reader. Dalal points out that Jung refers to his fundamental concepts of the collective unconscious and individuation when commenting on other cultures and ethnicities and raises the question of whether it is enough for post-Jungians to position him in history as a man of his time, without examining the possible racist roots of these theories.

Dalal's paper was first printed in the *British Journal of Psychotherapy* in 1988. It took thirty years until, in 2018, an open letter was published in the same journal (Baird et al., 2018) signed by thirty-five Jungian analysts and academics formally responding to Dalal. The letter calls on all involved in analytical psychology to critique and revise theories that harm people of colour and to apologise for actual damage done. The letter has received mixed response within the international Jungian community. A critique of the arguments against it are summarised and challenged by Andrew Samuels in his 2018 article, 'Jung and "Africans": A Critical and Contemporary Review of Some of the Issues'.

The collective unconscious

It is tempting to contend that, like Freud, Jung is a 'man of his times' and discard what is distasteful to modern ears without letting it trouble the essential concepts. Whilst I do not argue that the racist elements in earlier writings negates all of the value of some remarkable and original thinking, I do believe that a too-easy blanking out of what were key assumptions within the origins of the theory risks an unwitting re-enforcement of implicit racist structures in our own minds, as well as in the minds of others. Many modern-day Jungians argue that the concept of a *collective* unconscious, common to all humanity beneath and beyond the *personal* unconscious of the individual, means that the theory provides an anti-racist structure by stressing the commonality of all humanity and offering a global connectivity which is missing in Freudian theory. Potentially it does, but I suggest that a too-complacent attitude is misplaced, and we must take care.

Intrinsic to the concept of the collective unconscious and the archetypal structures is that they are timeless, immutable and universal. And it is this theory that lies behind Jung's dogmatic assertions about Africans and Asians, so for us to try to solve our problem by seeing Jung's statements as merely contextual and contingent is problematic.

Reading some of Jung's statements about people from Africa, the Middle East, India and Mexico, one can appreciate Fanon's distaste as expressed in the quote earlier in this chapter. Samuels (2018) cites the example where Jung is speaking about a bushman hunter:

> A bushman had a little son whom he loved with the tender monkey-love characteristic of primitives. Psychologically, this love is completely auto-erotic – that is to say, the subject loves himself in the object. The object serves as a sort of erotic mirror. One day the bushman came home in a rage; he had been fishing and had caught nothing. As usual the little fellow came running to meet him, but his father seized hold of him and wrung his neck on the spot. Afterwards, of course, he mourned for the dead child with the same unthinking abandon that had brought about his death.
>
> (Jung, 1921, CW 6, para. 403)

These interpretations of the bushman are breath-taking, not only in their content, but also in their certitude. As Samuels points out, the anthropologist Paul Radin, author of the 1927 book *Primitive Man as Philosopher*, knew Jung. He was 'a colleague of Jung's, taught at the Jung Institute, and invited Jung to write a response to his work on the Trickster. He was a Jungian, but he turned a critical Jungian' (Samuels, 2018, p. 5).

Samuels (2018) then quotes what Radin wrote (in 1927) about the above quote:

> No greater distortion of the facts could possibly be imagined. And yet Dr Jung obtained this example from what purported to be a first-hand account . . . [it] illustrates the unconscious bias that lies at the bottom of our judgement of primitive mentality, the unconscious assumption of the lack of differentiation and integration to be found there. . . . That an example like the one used by Jung should in all good faith be given as representative of the normal or even the abnormal reactions of a primitive man to a given emotional situation, shows the depth of ignorance that still exists on this subject (Radin, 1927, pp. 39 and 63).
>
> (p. 6)

It seems that Jung's mind was made up and he took no notice of this challenge, so the description remains. So be it. My concern now is how the consequent legacy has contributed to the making of our own minds.

The archetypal structures are unknowable directly and are unrepresentable. If we stay with the idea of archetypes as *predispositions*, then they are represented in the conscious mind as images which have been filtered through the personal but also the social, cultural and political layers. Thus, whilst the archetypal structure may be regarded as immutable, the form they take as *image* is dependent on the social and political context of the time. The image is *not* the archetype and, if we confuse the two, we appropriate the weightiness of the archetypal structure to support and justify unconscious prejudices. What is, in fact, a stereotype becomes fixed as if it were archetypal.

Postcolonial critic Homi Bhabha (1994) writes:

> An important feature of colonial discourse is its dependence on the concept of 'fixity' in the ideological construction of otherness. . . . Likewise the stereotype, which is its major discursive strategy, is a form of knowledge and identification that vacillates between what is always 'in place', already known, and something that must be anxiously repeated.
>
> (pp. 94–95)

In a previous paper (Morgan, 2002), I point out that, despite his own warnings, Jung misuses the idea of archetypes to reinforce his prejudice when writing of socalled primitive people. I argue that this 'primitive' state of mind for Jung

> became fixed to the external object, to the modern black African and to the risk he referred to as 'going black'. He filled out the 'primordial image' with 'the material of the conscious experience', with cultural and personal projections and used it as a justification for his own fears and fantasies. Unfortunately, he also loaded his conclusions about Africans, Asians, African Americans and others with all the weight of his influence and of the universality of the archetype.
>
> (p. 579)

This is a too-easy mistake to make when talking about archetypes. When we speak of something being 'archetypal' or an aspect of the 'collective unconscious', we do so from within a particular discourse and mindset. That mindset, like Jung's, is determined by the cultural and political context in which we grow up and inhabit. We can never be outside it. We can work to recognise some of the bias of the context, but we always bring with us a set of assumptions of which we are not aware, assumptions which are part and parcel of the cultural and social context of our lives. So, yes, Jung and Freud *were* of their times – but so are we of ours.

In recent years attention has been paid to this problem of bias which affects other areas of our theories – most notably in the matter of gender and sexuality. Fuller exploration is beyond the scope of this book, but it is interesting how a dis-ease with some of the more traditional writings has led to a much needed re-visioning of some important concepts, as I have written about in a previous paper (Morgan, 2000):

Archetypal structures are not essential 'truths' so much as potentialities that can be unfolded into and through the image. Oedipus then can be regarded as an image of one archetypal potential amongst a whole pantheon. Lacan (1987) and feminist psychoanalytic thinkers have attempted to return the myth to its original symbolic function, as a signifier, rather than the signified, calling it 'the name of the father' rather than the father himself.

(p. 69)

Lately the theory of archetypes has been challenged by a number of contemporary Jungian theorists from a variety of perspectives. Warren Colman (2016) suggests: 'It is not necessary to presuppose any kind of "super mind" if psychological life can be rooted in social life. The phenomena of the collective unconscious can be explained in social and material terms without requiring an ill-defined notion of a "collective psyche"' (p. 117). Jean Knox (2003) revises the concept of the archetype through the core themes of attachment and what she refers to as the 'emerging mind'. A full exploration of the main debates can be found in Hogenson (2004) and Colman (2016).

If one is keen to hold onto the concept of the archetype, then Jung's own warning needs heeding:

Again and again I encounter the mistaken notion that an archetype is determined in regard to its content, in other words that it is an unconscious idea (if such an expression be admissible). It is necessary to point out once more that archetypes are not determined as regards their content, but only as regards their form and then only to a very limited degree. A primordial image is determined as to its content only when it has become conscious and is therefore filled out with the material of conscious experience.

(1938, CW 9i, para. 155)

Like many others I came to Jungian thinking in my search for a meta-psychological theory that includes connection and a space for creativity and spirituality, and I continue to believe there is much in the bones of Jung's ideas which is of value. But I have come to see it also has the potential for application in ways that can be disturbing and dangerous. The collective unconscious is a stratum that exists at a profound level, but it is so large and so deep I am increasingly uncertain as to the value of the idea in understanding daily personal, social and political life. It is too easy to trivialise and exploit the gods so that, before we know it, they have shifted into stereotypes. Like Jung we are always in danger of localising the concept away from its global reach with our Eurocentric blind spot – a limitation that was there from the beginning with such a heavy reliance on Greek and Roman mythology to flesh out the archetypal. This is a focus expanded by Alan Vaughan (2019) in his consideration of African images and, in particular, the Kemetic-Egyptian deity Maat, which he argues offers 'a transcendent position from which to critique the inequities and constitutional jurisprudence that structured American apartheid' (p. 320).

Vaughan goes on to make a number of recommendations of changes that training organisations need to make, which includes '[c]urricula to include: comparative creation mythologies, ethnocultural historiographies and ethnographies' (p. 342).

Joseph Henderson (1988) delineated the cultural level between the archetypal and personal strata of the psyche, suggesting the concept of the *cultural unconscious*. As Singer and Kimbles (2004) write:

> Henderson notes that 'much of what Jung called personal was actually culturally conditioned' (1990, p. 104) and Adams says that 'much of what Jung called collective was cultural' (1996, p. 40). The concept of the cultural unconscious allows us to begin to become conscious of the connective tissue in which group life is lived out, embodied and structured both within and outside the individual. We can become better participant observers.
>
> (p. 184)

More limited than the collective, the cultural unconscious is less open to misuse and distortion. It is also more applicable as we struggle to understand the complexities of the socio-political aspects of our modern world, including the problem of racism. The concepts of the *cultural complex*, the *racial complex* and the *phantom narratives* that Kimbles introduces are also helpful and will be explored further in the next chapter.

Decolonising the theory

Brickman (2018) suggests that linking the unconscious to a developmental framework is itself problematic and we might be well served by loosening the tie between the two, a tie which is so connected to the distorted historic evolutionary ideas that underpin our current theories, 'by disengaging the unconscious from an evolutionary/developmental framework, psychoanalysis can begin to shed its racist baggage and use its performative abilities in the service of its ever powerful potential for the alleviation of mental suffering' (p. 233).

Hillman (1986) argues that the Jungian theory of opposites keep us pinned to a perspective of the world that is inevitably racist:

> Through serving the aim of self-correction, the ideas of shadow and unconscious maintain the theory of opposites and locate consciousness with light, day, bright, active etc. And so the entire modern psychological effort to raise consciousness, and the ego drafted to enact the endeavour, is one more manifestation of whiteness, perpetuating the very fault it would resolve. The project can never succeed since the unconscious it would redeem lies in the instrument of its intent; in the eye of its light.
>
> (p. 46)

Taken seriously, such challenges unsettle and disturb. But they can also stimulate by jangling the mind and shaking us up and questioning taken-for-granted ways of thinking. It's a question of whether we have sufficient confidence in the robustness of the core principles of psychoanalytic and Jungian analytic theory to trust that they can withstand some rattling. If we can loosen our transference to our founding fathers and let them rest in their own era, we can acknowledge their flaws and allow the possibility of re-visioning and re-energising our theoretical base.

Vaughan's second recommendation for the profession is for an engagement with

> Post-Jungian critiques of Jung's cultural biases, biases in research methodologies and his racism towards Africans, African Americans and others. The rationale that they were the products of his times, diminishes the growth prospects and utility of analytical psychology in the 21st century and forward. This is the work of our time.
>
> (2019, p. 342)

References

Adams, M.V. (1996) *The Multi-cultural Imagination: 'Race', Colour and the Unconscious.* London: Routledge.

Bhabha, H.K. (1994) *The Location of Culture.* Oxon: Routledge.

Baird, D., et al. (2018) Open Letter from a Group of Jungians on the Question of Jung's Writings on and Theories about Africans. *British Journal of Psychotherapy,* 34(4), 673–678.

Brewster, F. (2013) Wheel of Fire: The African American Dreamer and Cultural Unconsciousness. *Jung Journal: Culture and Psyche,* 7(1), 70–87.

Brewster, F. (2017) *African Americans and Jungian Psychology. Leaving the Shadows.* London: Routledge.

Brickman, C. (2018) *Race in Psychoanalysis. Aboriginal Populations in the Mind.* Oxon & New York: Routledge.

Colman, W. (2016) *Act and Image. The Emergence of Symbolic Imagination.* New Orleans, LA: Spring Journal Inc.

Dalal, F. (1988) Jung: A Racist. *British Journal of Psychotherapy,* 4(3), 263–279.

Fanon, F. (1986) *Black Skin, White Masks.* London: Pluto Press (First published in 1952 by Editions de Seuil).

Freud, S. (1913) Totem and Taboo: Some Points of Agreement Between the Mental Lives of Savages and Neurotics. *The Origin of Religion: Totem and Taboo, Moses and Monotheoism and Other Works.* Vol 13. London: Penguin.

Frosh, S. (2017) Primitivity and Violence: Traces of the Unconscious in Psychoanalysis. *Journal of Theoretical and Philosophical Psychology,* 37(1), 34–47.

Henderson, J. (1988) The Cultural Unconscious. *Quadrant: Journal of the C. G. Jung Foundation for Analytical Psychology,* 21(2), 7–16.

Henderson, J. (1990) The Cultural Unconscious. In *Shadow and Self.* Wilmette, IL: Chiron Publications.

Hillman, J. (1986) Notes on White Supremacy. Essaying an Archetypal Account of Historical Events. *Spring Publications,* 29, 58.

Hogenson, G. (2004) Archetypes: Emergence and the Psyche's Deep Structure. *Analytical Psychology: Contemporary Perspectives in Jungian Analysis*. Hove, East Sussex: Brunner Routledge.

Jung, C.G. (1921) The Type Problem in Poetry. *Psychological Types*. The Collected Works of C. G. Jung. Vol. 6. London and Princeton, NJ: Routledge & Kegan Paul/Princeton University Press.

Jung, C.G. (1935) *The Symbolic Life*. Collected Works 18. Princeton, NJ: Princeton University Press.

Jung, C.G. (1938) Psychological Aspects of the Mother Archetype. *The Archetypes and the Collective Unconscious*. Collected Works 9i. Princeton, NJ: Princeton University Press.

Jung, C.G. (1939) The Dreamlike World of India. *Civilization in Transition*. Collected Works 10. Princeton, NJ: Princeton University Press.

Jung, C.G. (1948) Healing the Split. *The Symbolic Life*. Collected Works 18. Princeton, NJ: Princeton University Press.

Jung, C.G. (1963) *Memories, Dreams and Reflections*. New York: Pantheon.

Knox, J. (2003) *Archetype, Attachment, Analysis. Jungian Psychology and the Emergent Mind'*. Hove, East Sussex: Brunner-Routledge.

Lacan, J. (1987) *The Four Fundamental Concepts of Psycho-analysis.* London: Peregrine Books.

Morgan, H. (2000) Modern Western Society. The Making of Myth and Meaning. *Jungian Thought in the Modern World*. Eds: Christopher, E., and McFarland Solomon, H. London: Free Association Books.

Morgan, H. (2002) Exploring Racism. *Journal of Analytical Psychology*, 47(4), 567–581.

Radin, P. (1927) *Primitive Man as Philosopher*. Reprinted by New York Review of Books Classics (2017). Oxford: Blackwell.

Samuels, A. (2018) Jung and 'Africans': A Critical and Contemporary Review of Some of the Issues. *International Journal of Jungian Studies*, 10, 2.

Shamdasani, S. (2003) *Jung and the Making of Modern Psychology. The Dream of a Science*. Cambridge: Cambridge University Press.

Singer, T., and Kimbles, S. (2004) The Emerging Theory of Cultural Complexes. *Analytical Psychology. Contemporary Perspectives in Jungian Analysis*. Eds: Cambray, J., and Carter, L. Hove, Sussex and New York: Routledge.

Vaughan, A. (2019) African American Cultural History and Reflection on Jung in the African Diaspora. *Journal of Analytical Psychology*, 64(3), 320–348.

Chapter 6

The racial complex

The village sign

A friend whom I shall call Peter lives in a large village in the English countryside. His garden wall runs along part of the main road through the middle of the village. There is considerable wealth in the area alongside pockets of rural poverty. The predominantly white population of around 2,500 people includes fifteen to twenty people of colour: care workers, owners and staff of the local Indian and the Chinese restaurants and two doctors.

At the start of the Black Lives Matter protests in May 2020, Peter was walking through the village when he came across a couple of teenage neighbours he knew, who were holding makeshift 'Black Lives Matter' placards. The girls explained that they were not allowed to attend the BLM protests in a nearby town due to the Covid-19 pandemic, and Peter offered to construct a larger billboard and erect it just inside his garden wall so they could paint a more substantial poster for the site that would be visible from the road. Accordingly, the board was built and assembled, and the girls spent an afternoon painting a simple sign asserting 'Black Lives Matter'. An elderly couple approached Peter, saying they were really pleased the board was up as they had three mixed race grandchildren and 'nobody talks about it'.

About a week later a neighbour called in to tell Peter that she had seen a white woman get out of her car and start hitting and kicking the board, which then toppled over. When the neighbour confronted the woman and asked what she was doing, she angrily asserted that she had to drive past the sign every day and she wasn't having her daughters being repeatedly told that their lives didn't matter. Her two children, aged about 4 and 6, were in the car watching her. She then got back in the car and drove off.

Peter set to work to mend and re-erect the sign. However, a week later during the night it was attacked again, and this time completely destroyed and taken away. The village has a local Facebook site and within hours it was buzzing with comments raising a variety of different views on the subject. This included some explicitly racist 'go back home' comments that the moderator decided to take down. Many expressed a similar concern to the woman who originally attacked the board: asserting that black lives matter assumes that white lives don't. There were a few comments about white men who had been killed in police custody so 'what's the problem', and many claimed that all lives matter and we are all the same. Some postings, mostly but not exclusively from the younger members of the village, were fully supportive of the board and had welcomed its presence. This privileged rural setting, comfortably distanced from the travails of urban life, was suddenly thrust into the fray. A conversation had started.

The Black Lives Matter (BLM) movement came together in 2013 when George Zimmerman was acquitted of murder after he shot Trayvon Martin dead as he was walking back from a corner shop in Florida. Following the shooting of Breonna Taylor by Louisville police in March 2020 and the death two months later of George Floyd as a police officer knelt on his neck, there was a surge of energy within the movement and across the globe.

It is interesting how the apparently simple – and one might think uncontentious – statement that black lives matter raises such a reaction within the white population. Writing in *Prospect* magazine, July 3, 2020, Arianne Shahvisi suggests that the tag-line for the Black Lives Matter movement 'expresses mournfulness and anger, but also yearning' and that it points to two things:

1   As far as various major social institutions are concerned – the police, the criminal justice system, medicine – Black lives don't matter as much as other lives.
2   Black lives *should* matter as much as other lives.

Taken together, these statements form the basis for challenging anti-Black racism.

The first point is a *descriptive* statement. It *describes* the world, and its truth can be verified through data based on observations. In the UK, Black people are five times more likely to die in childbirth than white people, and Black infant mortality is twice as high. Black people are twice as likely as white people to be unemployed, and almost half of Black households live in poverty. Black people are ten times more likely to be stopped and searched than white people, and four times more likely to be arrested. They constitute 3 per cent of the population, but 8 per cent of deaths in police custody. Black lives are deplorably under-valued. . . . Turning to the second claim, 'Black lives *should* matter' is what we call a normative statement. It's a moral proclamation, stating it's wrong that Black lives are under-valued. Moral statements cannot be verified by observations; they're based on particular values that must be argued for.

(p. 1. Italics in original)

The response that 'white lives matter', as was written on a banner flown over a football game in Burnley, Lancashire after footballers had knelt in support of BLM, assumes the movement is claiming that *only* black lives matter. The corollary, the assertion that 'white lives matter', is that *only* white lives matter. The point is white lives already matter, whereas it seems that black lives do not.

This means the statement 'all lives matter', often used by white people as an attempt to smooth over the problem, whilst clearly untrue, looks like an attempt to manage the situation and avoid thought and action. Shahvisi says:

> Note that nobody was saying 'All Lives Matter' before 2013. Rather, it's a direct response to BLM, and has no life outside that. And that's a problem, because if BLM is understood as a commitment to urgently tackling the violence and brutality of anti-Black racism, then blurting that 'All Lives Matter' is at best, tangential, and at worst, a malevolent distraction. Its effect is to stall conversations about anti-Black racism and instead either pretend that all lives do matter, or talk about everybody's lives all at once, whether or not particular groups are subject to particular, potentially fatal injustices right now. This leaves no bandwidth to address the particularly brutal injustices that Black people face. Saying 'All Lives Matter' violates the concept of triage in medical ethics, which demands that we address the most troubling or life-endangering issues first.
>
> 'All Lives Matter' is therefore an obstacle to tackling anti-Black racism. Sometimes, it's a result of ignorance, a misinterpretation of BLM. More often, it's intentional; a filibuster, bent on derailing anti-racist work.
>
> (p. 1)

This predominantly white village in England's prosperous green belt might be considered an exemplar of white privilege. A key element of the privilege of whiteness is that it is upheld through an implicit contract between white people and is kept invisible so matters of race and racism are not to be discussed except as a problem elsewhere. As Adrienne Harris (2019) puts it, such a pact

> is relatedness dominated by dissociation, amnesia and disavowal. In essence, it is a refusal to imagine a shared humanity. . . . Very often, [when] the ugly underpinnings of this pact are revealed, they are not taken on within the white communities as phenomena to be understood and worked on within and by the white community.
>
> (p. 311)

The billboard, with its deceptively simple message, intruded into this pastoral white collusion. Its effect was to disrupt and make explicit the tacit contract that lay beneath an aspect of how this community functions. The response for some was outrage and a need to tear down the offending sign and reinstate the pact. Interestingly, of course, things cannot now be returned to where they were. Certain matters are out in the open and they cannot be closed off again. As I write the sign has not gone up again, but I suggest it doesn't need to. The site of the billboard, the fact that it was present and had been torn down, is powerful. For a while, at least, it is a present absence.

The social unconscious

Psychoanalytic perspectives on how racism works in the psyche and its impact on those on the receiving end tend to rely on the concepts of projection, splitting and introjection. This is helpful as far as it goes but it can cut the individual off from the social and the political context. We need ways to think about the connectivity between people and how racial identity impacts on our internal as well as our social world.

Linda Alcoff (2015) writes: 'Whiteness is lived and not merely represented. It is a prominent feature of one's way of being in the world, of how one navigates that world, and of how one is navigated around by others' (p. 9). She goes on to suggest that we tend to reject group concepts in order to maintain the idea that we have control over our identity:

> Being identified in a way that lies beyond our individual control conflicts with individualist ideas, and illusions, about our autonomy. The real concern with race may be less the faulty presumptions about genetic difference than the fact that this is a social fact about us, with social meanings and implications over which we have limited agency. People of color have largely come to accept this; for whites, the forcible interpellations of their racial identity are more often a new experience.
>
> (p. 21)

The usual psychoanalytic division between inner and outer is problematic in formulating an understanding of how connective processes work at an unconscious level across groups so that unified dynamics are accepted and maintained. This approach tends to reinforce the individualism that liberal white people prefer, as Alcoff describes. We are a lot more comfortable thinking in terms of the individual racist act that we can then dissociate ourselves from. But the division of the races was created by a racist system for the economic and political purposes of justifying slavery and colonisation. It is a deep, entrenched social structure which creates and promotes white privilege and is one within which we all live. No one can be free from it. The statement 'I am not a racist' is meaningless in such a system.

Farhad Dalal (1998) challenges the distinction between the individual and the social unconscious, arguing that we are created by and through the social. He distinguishes the concept from that of the Jungian collective unconscious as well as the group analytic theories of the unconscious life of groups. I cannot do justice here to his argument, but his stress on the way power relations are structured within the social unconscious is important. He says:

The social unconscious contains, among other things, several deceits. One of these deceits is the disguising of power relations . . . [it] is a representation of the institutionalization of social power relations in the structure of the psyche itself. In this sense it is a bridge between the social and the psychological.

(pp. 209–210)

W.E.B. Du Bois (1940) writes:

My own study of psychology under William James had pre-dated the Freudian era, but it had prepared me for it. I now began to realize that in the fight against race prejudice, we were not facing simply the rational, conscious determination of white folk to oppress us; we were facing age-long complexes sunk now largely to unconscious habit and irrational urge.

(p. 148)

The cultural complex

Sam Kimbles (2014), an African American Jungian analyst, sought to connect the analytical psychology of his training with his experiences of social and political dynamics. He asks: 'Is it possible, in our analytic understanding of healing, to include a wider attitude toward human suffering that encompasses the ever-present issues of poverty, social inequality, social breakdown, and violence?' (p. 79). In seeking an answer he brought together Joseph Henderson's (1988) delineation of a level between the archetypal and personal strata of the psyche which he called the *cultural unconscious*, and Jung's theory of the individual *complexes* which came out of his experimental work between 1904 and 1911 through the Word Association Test. Kimbles (2014) notes that 'it is important to recall that Jung, even before he formulated the notion of the archetypes, meant the term complex to describe patterns of interlocking associations grouped around emotionally toned themes and ideas' (p. 6).

Kimbles (2000) suggests these patterns could be seen in groups, communities and societies and names them *cultural complexes*. He writes that 'Cultural Complexes operate . . . through the group expectations, its definition of itself and sense of uniqueness. We can find the (group) complexes operating in and through the group's fears, enemies and its attitudes toward other groups' (p. 68). With his colleague Tom Singer, he edited a collection of works where the concept was applied.

Cultural complexes are dynamic relational systems that work through a group's beliefs and expectations of itself as well as its attitudes towards other groups:

Like individual complexes, cultural complexes tend to be repetitive, autonomous, resist consciousness, and collect experience that confirm their historical point of view. And . . . cultural complexes tend to be bipolar, so that when they are activated, the group ego or the individual ego of a group member becomes identified with one part of the unconscious cultural complex, while the other part is projected onto the suitable hook of another group or one of its members.

(Singer and Kimbles, 2004, p. 6)

Kimbles (2014) develops this further to describe the intergenerational transmission of cultural complexes through 'persuasive unconscious stories or phantom narratives' (p. 12), many of which are rooted in collective cultural trauma. He draws interesting parallels with Bion's (1961/1983) concept of 'proto-mental systems', which he sees as the 'theoretical root of my own view of phantom narratives as forming the organizing background of the mentation expressed by cultural complexes' (Kimbles, 2014, p. 9). He quotes Bion:

In order to explain the linkage between the one operative Basic Assumption, and at the same time to explain the fate of the inoperative Basic Assumptions, I proposed to postulate the existence of 'proto-mental' phenomena. The proto-mental system I visualize as one in which physical and psychological or mental are undifferentiated. It is a matrix from which spring the phenomena . . . it is from this matrix that emotions proper to the basic assumption flow to reinforce, pervade, and, on occasion, to dominate the mental life of the group (1961/1983, p. 102).

Kimbles sees these 'proto-mental systems' or phantom narratives as forming a background field which operate within the particular cultural and social context and which influence the individual thoughts, feelings and responses at an unconscious level.

Kimbles's fellow African American Jungian analyst Fanny Brewster (2020) specifically refers to the 'racial complex':

I believe that my discussion of an African American cultural racial complex, brought about by the trauma of the African Holocaust, and racism, is one avenue for looking at our deeply complicated American collective as well as individual problems in all three of these areas that Jung has posited – the therapeutic, the philosophical and the moral.

(p. 23)

At the centre of this racial complex is the division into black and white and the protection of white privilege with its characteristics of solipsism and white exceptionalism. The power differential within Western society makes the impact of this complex on our black citizens persistent, erosive and traumatic. For white people, the privilege bestowed by whiteness has to be kept hidden through silence, colour blindness and white fragility. As DiAngelo (2011) writes, 'white fragility' is a state in which even a minimum amount of racial stress becomes intolerable, triggering a range of defensive moves. These moves include the outward display of emotions such as anger, fear and guilt, and behaviors such as argumentation, silence, and leaving the stress-inducing situation. These behaviors, in turn, function to reinstate white racial equilibrium.

(p. 54)

As Bion states, in 'proto-mental' phenomena the physical and the mental are undifferentiated and so he asserts that we need to include the involvement of the body and the sexual along with the emotional. Since the beginning of the trade in enslaved Africans, the body of the black man and woman has been a source of fascination, desire, hatred, envy and fear for white people. Straker (2004) argues that racism utilises what she refers to as a *fantasy fetish*. She says

Bhabha (1983) believes that through stereotyping in this way, the dominant group uses the disparaged group in the mode of the fetish. In other words, the disparaged group, by being stereotyped and made to be the same, is used as an object or fetish to suspend disbelief in Otherness even while being cast as Other.

(p. 412)

For Straker this reinforces the link she makes between racism and perversion.

This connection is also made by Adrienne Harris (2019) who, in her development of an understanding of how racism operates and white privilege maintained, turned to the concept of the *perverse pact* first proposed by Ruth Stein (2005). Whilst acknowledging the controversial nature of the concept of perversion, Stein (2005) suggests that there is 'a special case of perverse modes of object-relatedness and responses to the demands of reality'. This, she says, 'often manifests itself as a disguised, often sexualized, enactment of hatred and destructiveness which is actualized within a relational structure, what I call the "perverse pact"' (p. 776).

Harris (2019) writes:

This pact can be observed in individuals, in couples, in social formations, and in intersubjective space. What is powerful in this concept is Stein's attention to social links that are both very close and intimate and simultaneously very violent and drenched in hostility. Both terms – 'perverse' and 'pact' – are necessary ingredients.

(p. 309)

She emphasises that this 'perverse pact' 'is not between white people and people of color. It is a pact, lived out consciously and unconsciously, within white culture and in the individual consciousness of white persons. It is a pact that underwrites racism' (p. 311).

Bringing these strands together offers the possibility of a wider perspective of the intricate web of internal and group dynamics that operates to ensure the continuation of the status quo and might go some way in explaining the stubborn resistance to change despite protestations and the apparent desire for a more equitable society.

The doctor's surgery

I turn now to an event described in the book *Borderline Welfare* (2005) by Andrew Cooper and Julian Lousada.

> Over a considerable period of time a psychotherapy patient recalled the following events. He was seven, and he and his mother were leaving their GP's consulting room. As he passed through the waiting room he inadvertently trod on a woman's foot. 'Can't you look where you are going, you stupid little n****r!' she snarled. His mother quickly bundled him out. He knew he wanted his mother to stand up for him and in some way hit back. The patient went on to describe how he had grown up knowing about incidents like this. He knew how to recognize the racist thug; he could see them coming, and in his family he had learnt in countless ways to be watchful and on guard.
>
> (p. 88)

The patient relates that, although the GP overheard the eruption, and although there were others in the waiting room – both black and white – no one made any sort of intervention other than his mother hurrying him out.

Until the moment of the attack in the surgery, the boy and his mother, the GP and the patients in the waiting room including the woman, were all present as persons and it might be assumed that racial differences were not especially to the fore. However, given the racial complex of the culture in which the event took place, the fact that it lay dormant and hidden does not mean it was without effect. The woman's words broke into and disrupted the moment with a violence, activating the complex. Each individual within the scenario had a different relationship to the complex depending where each was situated in relation to the power dynamics of race. By using the language she did, she rent asunder any sense of equivalence, forcing the crude, brutal cut of a black/white binary between the boy and the woman but also across the room. No longer was there just a room of patients in varying degrees of pain and anxiety; the racist thuggery had forced itself to the surface and now there was 'black' and there was 'white' and each were called upon for a response.

Cooper and Lousada continue with the account:

> Some days later, he was once more with his mother when the same woman spotted them and came running over. 'Oh, I am so glad to see you, I wanted to apologise for my outburst – I just went out of my mind'. The woman looked

relieved, pleased, and expectant of forgiveness. Far from being reassured by this second encounter, the patient found himself feeling more tentative and anxious as if now he could never be adequately prepared for what might happen next. The hateful outburst was in some sense more insidious because it cohabited with guilt, but not in such a way as to inhibit the outburst. To make matters worse he had come to understand that *both* he and this woman had been the subject of an ambush – she from within, and himself from without. The capacity to preserve a mind capable of striving for a coexistence with the other is replaced with a mind that protects itself by annihilating or attacking and denigrating the other.

(pp. 88–89. Italics in original)

The boy

By the age of 7 the boy was already familiar with the experience of being identified with the negative end of the projective dynamic of the unconscious racial complex and had learnt to expect what he described as racist thugs. He knew how to recognise them, to anticipate possible threatening behaviour and develop strategies to deal with them. If the incident in the surgery had not been followed up by the apology, he could have categorised the woman in his mind as one such racist. By apologising, by explaining her behaviour as being out of her mind, the boy discovered that there were a variety of states of mind within what Cooper and Lousada call 'the psychic geography of racism'. Some of these states are more toxic than others but they are clearly interwoven. This now leaves the boy in a hazardous state in a wide-open landscape where the 'ambush' might come from any unexpected quarter.

Narendra Keval (2016), referring to another incident, describes how the patient's 'immediate predicament is shaped by his experience of the White world at large, in which people going about their ordinary lives can experience a moment of madness in which racist thinking and feeling confronts them or ambushes their ordinary sensibilities' (p. 46).

Fakhry Davids (2011) follows the same theme:

> Writing in another time and place, Frantz Fanon (1952 [1986]) characterized this use of one's blackness . . . as forcefully tossing the black person into an arid area of non-being from which he has, somehow, to gather together once more the now-fractured strands of his being.

(p. 3)

For the person on the receiving end, these 'moments of madness' must themselves be experienced as maddening in that the process is a factor of something within the perpetrator's mind and not of the relationship between them. If the woman had responded to the boy's clumsiness with an understandable crossness but without racialising the incident, she would have been reacting to him and what he had done. It would still have been an unpleasant interaction, but its cause would have been apparent to both. By linking his clumsiness to his colour, a violence entered the engagement which resulted in the depersonalisation of the child, who is now lost behind a generalised wall of blackness.

The mother

We don't know why the mother didn't confront the woman but bundled her son out of the surgery. This entirely unexpected outburst would have also come as a shock to her and may well have ambushed *her* thinking. Her reaction was flight. It could have been fight, but I imagine that previous experience led to an anxiety that further confrontation would escalate, and she would be labelled as 'an angry black woman'. Perhaps she had little confidence in the support of the doctor or the other patients and things could get worse for herself and her son. Paradoxically, if the woman had shouted 'you stupid boy', it might have been easier for the mother to object, for this would be a matter of a woman defending her son from an over-reaction to what was, after all, an accident. The use of the 'N' word made the racist nature of the attack crystal clear and consequently raised the stakes and the tension. Now any response is from a *black* woman to a *white* one, and the mother's experience may well have led her to a conviction that she would not come off well in such a confrontation. Whilst others in a similar situation may well have acted differently, her instinct was to protect her son by getting him out and away from the situation as quickly as possible.

The black bystanders

We are told there were other patients, both black and white, in the waiting room at the time of the incident. The racist attack brought the colour aspects of these people's identities to the fore along with that of the boy. For the black bystanders, I can only speculate that similar internal dynamics were operating in relation to their own history of being on the receiving end of racism as I suggest were going on in the mother. For them to step in and confront the woman would require taking the risk of escalation and danger.

I am aware this is a rather cursory exploration of the black experience of the incident, partly as it is necessarily speculation on my part and partly because, for the purpose of this chapter, I am concerned to examine the responses of the various white players in the scenario to tease out the possible underlying dynamics.

The woman

Because of the apology in the street which took place later, we know that this woman is not an avowed white supremacist. Apparently, she feels a sense of shame and wants to apologise, although in doing so she is entirely unaware how this complicates and confuses matters for the boy, who now has the established distinctions in his mind challenged.

What, then, was this 'ambush' inside the mind of the woman that took place the instant the boy trod on her foot, and where did it come from? I am assuming the foot that was tripped over was damaged and the cause of her visit to the GP, so that someone treading on it caused considerable pain. Cooper and Lousada again:

> What the patient discovered in the woman . . . was how thin-skinned she was when in pain. Without thinking, her response was not to remonstrate with him about his carelessness but rather attack him for his blackness, as if the two were necessarily associated.
>
> (2005, p. 93)

Particularly shocking is her choice of language. We know what this word implies in the mouth of a white person. We know its horrific history and what therefore is conjured up when it is used. Or at least we should.

The idea that repressed unconscious material may force its way to the surface in the form of an enactment at any time – but especially when the individual is anxious or in pain – is a familiar one within psychoanalysis. Psychoanalytic theories inform us how such eruptions can make use of racist dynamics to project the unwanted aspects of the self on the racialised other who is then feared, hated or envied. Keval (2016) stresses this is by no means a simplistic unified process and notes the

> complex motives and functions of retreating into the racist state of mind, which differs from one patient to the next. Their multi-layered losses culminated in grievances and hatreds that coalesced and sought expression in a predatory, socially sanctioned, and opportunistic structure in racism which served to bind their emotional turmoil.
>
> (p. 120)

Quoting Lane (1998, p. 6), he says: 'In this way, when the shadow of the object of grievance is projected onto the ethnic other, he presents a long awaited opportunity for the subject to enact the appalling displays of violence that heretofore have existed only internally' (Keval, 2016, p. 120).

Keval suggests that

> One configuration of this internal situation is a defensive or narcissistic organisation in the mind that Rosenfeld (1971) has called a 'psychic gang', an amalgam of attitudes which create an ambience of brutality, with omnipotence, arrogance, cruelty, thuggery and violence as part of its working.
>
> (p. 22)

Any overt and active display of racism exposes the raw, brutal nature of its roots. This is the case whether it is a deliberate, conscious expression of avowed white supremacists, or it erupts in the mind of an individual such as the woman in the surgery who would not normally align herself with that group. This crude black-and-white position splits and simplifies any possibility of complex thinking and demands instead a gesture, an action to externalise and make concrete an internal thuggery. In the case of the woman there was an eruption, an ambush that overwhelmed her. She did indeed 'lose her mind' in that it bypassed thought. Nevertheless, the 'psychic gang' must have been already present and waiting for this moment.

The woman is keen to apologise and grateful for the opportunity to do so when she encounters the boy and his mother later in the street. As discussed in Chapter 4, genuine, 'healthy' guilt consists of an acknowledgement and remorse that one has done damage to the other and a wish to make reparation in order to repair the relationship. However, it seems the apology is designed to make the woman feel better about herself and indicates a lack of the necessary work that is required in effective reparation. Indeed, we know that, for the boy, the apology does further harm. We don't have the woman's version of the events, just the patient's memory, but Stephen Mitchell's (2000) notion of 'guiltiness' as opposed to guilt as discussed in Chapter 4 seems applicable.

There is violence in all forms of racism, and an active, anti-racist position demands that we do not hide behind a liberal persona by splitting ourselves off from these extreme instances of brutality. I *think* I would not use the language that erupted from the woman – even writing the word she used feels deeply uncomfortable. However, to live in any society is to be affected by and implicated in its cultural complexes, and the racial complex involves us all. We cannot find a place to stand outside of it and we are all pulled into its drama when it surfaces. That is not to say we do not have choice, but we need to be aware of the underlying dynamic and the effort required to resist its pull. I am interested, therefore, in the other white figures on the scene and the parts they play.

The doctor

We are not told in the vignette whether the doctor was white or a person of colour. If he was black or brown, I speculate his failure to intervene would have been due to the same reticence as that of the black patients in the room. For the purpose of this exploration, I will assume that he was white.

The patient was sure that the doctor had heard the incident and yet had not intervened. 'The General Practitioner who had always shown interest and concern in the patient failed to protect him. For the patient, it was as if this symbolic agent of justice . . . chose to look the other way' (Cooper & Lousada, 2005, p. 98). It is possible that the doctor spoke to the woman after the event when she came in for her appointment, but that misses the point. The boy needed to see authority – in this case represented by the doctor – make a public intervention. A container was required which made clear that any 'ambush', such as had occurred, would be acknowledged and the perpetrator reprimanded so that the hatred might be detoxified.

What ties the perpetrator and the victim together in an endless and deadly interchange is precisely the failure of justice. . . . Never should we underestimate the consequences of the failure of justice, because it leads to the conversion of the wish for retribution to the wish for revenge.

(p. 99)

As the person in authority, the GP was in the position to administer justice by confronting the woman, thus establishing for everyone present that she was in the wrong and racism would not be accepted in the surgery; it was to be maintained as a safe place. White disavowal serves to keep apart the racist thought from the conviction that we are good people. In between is a silent abyss. By shattering the pretence of colour blindness, the woman's words exposed the defence and brought discomfort to the white people present. However much the doctor may have identified with the boy and disapproved of the woman's words, he was also complicit in the 'perverse pact', the relational structure among white people ensuring silent complicity. To actively break this contract, to speak out and challenge racism risks exposing the disavowal, the basic fault at the centre of whiteness and thus alienating oneself from the comfort of conformity. The perception of non-racist 'goodness' is a passive one and evades the active anti-racist stance that would have been required for the doctor to intervene.

The demonstrations across the world against racism prompted by the murder of George Floyd protest against the brutality enacted against Floyd as well as many, many others. They also highlight the historic and repeated failures of societies to recognise the enormity of the damage done by racism. Anger against centuries of slavery that has gone unacknowledged, as well as present day inequity in education, employment, health, housing, etc. erupts onto our streets in a collective roar for justice.

When authority fails to act, as was the case with the GP, there is an erosion of the civil contract between citizen and state. If any member of society has no confidence in the social system of justice, from the police to the courts to the prisons, then she or he is left exposed and vulnerable and the world becomes a terrifying and unpredictable place.

The white bystanders

What he could never come to terms with was the silence of the other patients. . . . What then was the relatedness between the bystanders, the angry outburst, and the act of reparation? None of the bystanders is involved, but all are seemingly caught in identification with the supposed 'victim'. What is evident here is collusion and fear manifesting itself as indifference. . . . It is as if the woman dazzled the other patients, the bystanders, who for a period were immobilized and perhaps even excited by her aggression.

(Cooper & Lousada, 2005, pp. 93–94)

I am assuming the same dynamics that operated within the doctor applied to the white patients in the room, without the additional demand of his position. They took on the role of bystander. In transactional analysis, Karpman's Drama Triangle describes the roles of 'persecutor', 'victim' and 'rescuer' that can form around conflict. I am told by social work colleagues that a fourth position has been added – that of the 'helpless bystander'. It is a role that can be taken up by those working with the traumatised, such as victims of torture. Carrying this role may be a defence against vicarious trauma or a form of burnout and it also offers a 'get out clause'. This sense of helplessness strikes me as a depressingly familiar position that white liberals take up when confronted with racism.

Kerry Novick (2018) writes:

> The role of the bystander is very important in understanding hostile actions and power relationships. . . . The perpetrator of violence demands that the bystander actively condone or at least passively allow abuse. The collusion on the part of the bystander makes the victim feel even more helpless and ready to resort to equally destructive or self-attacking behaviour to save himself.
>
> (p. 29)

Protestations of helplessness, of not knowing what to do, can frequently be heard among white liberal people. The consequence of this helplessness as a response is that there is no interruption of the aggression or abuse of the racist act. If we regard its unconscious purpose to condone and allow, then it can be seen as a disguised complicity that ensures the continuation of the status quo.

In the quote from Cooper and Lousada earlier, they suggest the bystanders in the surgery are caught in identification with the victim. In Chapter 2, Ryan Parker's (2019) research into attitudes of white people to slavery was discussed, where the participants could imagine themselves as the enslaved victim of terrible brutality but not as the perpetrator of the violence. If pressed to put themselves in the position of the slave owner, they imagined themselves as kindly and benign. An identification with the victim has the appearance of empathy and concern whilst not actually doing anything to help him. It also allows a disidentification with the woman whose action is condemned. The process of disavowal is facilitated in that the individual can *both* promote a view of oneself s good, *and* ensure white privilege persists.

End point

Like all complexes, the racial complex as an 'inoperative Basic Assumption' may lie unacknowledged at the level of the social unconscious until activated by an event. Kimbles (2014) writes that the 'activation of cultural complexes shows that emotional processes have already been transmuted into group and individual processes or formations that are structured by fears and anxieties around differences and similarities' (p. 9). Such fears and anxieties may lie dormant as was the case in the surgery prior to the racist eruption and in the village before the sign was erected. In both cases the cultural complex became activated and, because it is a group phenomenon, everyone is involved whether we like it or not. Whatever one does – including remaining silent – is determined by our relationship to the complex, but we cannot remain outside of it.

Harris (2019) asserts that racism is kept in place by a seemingly odd combination of dissociation and violence. The racist epithet used by the woman in the surgery did violence in depersonalising the boy. The later apology was her attempt to dissociate herself form the act, as was the silence of the white GP and bystanders. Both incidents point to a racist system which is deeply entrenched and covered over with invisibility and silence.

These are local incidents, whereas the murder of George Floyd and the global spread of the recording of his death became an international one. The violence done to this one man brought to the surface centuries of brutality against black people and its continuation today – a fact that is both well-known and dissociated from by white people. As has been stated, complexes tend to be bi-polar, whereby some members of society identify with one part and some with the other and we have certainly seen this division made powerfully visible across the globe. What is interesting is that this hasn't been just a black/white divide. Plenty of white people have also been out on the streets protesting, and the demand for justice has been expressed across our society – as, of course, has the backlash.

Whilst the statistics about how black people have been disadvantaged and harmed have been available for decades, there is possibly something about this latest uprising of anger and determination for change that carries hope. Kimbles reminds us that:

> One lesson of therapeutic group work is that awareness of the power of this *proto-mental* dynamic potentially frees up emotional energy for a different and more conscious kind of *work* in which the group can become the agent for more positive cultural change.
>
> (2014, p. 10. Italics in original)

He continues:

> We are invariably co-conspirators in the phantom narratives we inherit from past generations and intuit as important to our contemporaries. Our subjectivity is thus invariably more attuned to cultural complexes than we know and not as freed up as we would like to the activity of the present effort in each new generation to rethink the past and to discard what about it did not work. . . . If we can become conscious of this attunement to the self-perpetuating past, it allows us to see the cultural tradition as a potential space, a political arena that may become transitional to transformation.
>
> (p. 11)

References

Alcoff, L.M. (2015) *The Future of Whiteness*. Cambridge: Polity Press.

Bhabha, H.K. (1983) Difference, Discrimination and the Discourse of Colonialism. *The Politics of Theory*. Eds: Barker, F., Hulme, P., Iversen, D., and Loxley, D., 194–211. Colchester, UK: University of Essex.

Bion, W. (1961/1983) *Experiences in Groups*. London: Tavistock Publications.

Brewster, F. (2020) *The Racial Complex. A Jungian Perspective on Culture and Race*. Oxon and New York: Routledge.

Cooper, A., and Lousada, J. (2005) *Borderline Welfare. Feeling and Fear of Feeling in Modern Welfare*. London: H. Karnac (Books) Ltd.

Dalal, F. (1998) *Taking the Group Seriously: Towards a Post-Foulkesian Group Analytic Theory*. London: Jessica Kingsley Publishers.

Davids, F. (2011) *Internal Racism: A Psychoanalytic Approach to Race and Difference*. Basingstoke: Palgrave Macmillan.

DiAngelo, R. (2011) White Fragility. *International Journal of Critical Pedagogy*, 3(3), 54–70.

Du Bois, W.E.B. (2007) *Dusk of Dawn*. Oxford: Oxford University Press (First published in 1940 by Harcourt, Brace and World Inc.).

Fanon, F. (1986) *Black Skin, White Masks*. London: Pluto Press (First published in 1952 by Editions de Seuil).

Harris, A. (2019) The Perverse Pact: Racism and White Privilege. *American Imago*, 76(3), 309–333.

Henderson, J.L. (1988) The Cultural Unconscious. *Quadrant: Journal of the C. G. Jung Foundation for Analytical Psychology*, 21(2), 7–16.

Keval, N. (2016) *Racist States of Mind. Understanding the Perversion of Curiosity and Concern*. London: Karnac Books Ltd.

Kimbles, S. (2000) The Cultural Complex and the Myth of Invisibility. *The Vision Thing, Myth, Politics and Psyche in the World*. London: Routledge.

Kimbles, S. (2014) *Phantom Narratives: The Unseen Contributions of Culture to Psyche*. Lanham, MD: Rowman & Littlefield.

Lane, C. (1998) The Psychoanalysis of Race: An Introduction. *The Psychoanalysis of Race*. Ed: Lane, C., 1–37. New York: Columbia University Press.

Mitchell, S.A. (2000) You've Got to Suffer If You Want to Sing the Blues: Psychoanalytic Reflections on Guilt and Self-Pity. *Psychoanalytic Dialogues*, 10(5), 713–733.

Novick, K. (2018) Learning the Difference Between Hate and Violence. *Before and After Violence. Developmental, Clinical and Sociocultural Aspects*. Ed: Akhtar, S. London: Lexington Books.

Parker, R.N. (2019) Slavery in the White Psyche. *Psychoanalytic Social Work*, 26(1).

Rosenfeld, H. (1971) A Clinical Approach to the Psychoanalytic Theory of the Life and Death Instincts: An Investigation into the Aggressive Aspects of Narcissism. *International Journal of Psychoanalysis*, 52, 169–178.

Shahvisi, A. (2020) The Philosophical Flaw in Saying 'All Lives Matter'. *Prospect Magazine*, July.

Singer, T., and Kimbles, S. (2004) *The Cultural Complex: Contemporary Jungian Perspectives on Psyche and Society*. Hove: Routledge.

Stein, R. (2005) Why Perversion? 'False Love' and the Perverse Pact. *International Journal of Psychoanalysis*, 86(3), 775–799.

Straker, G. (2004) Race for Cover: Castrated Whiteness, Perverse Consequences. *Psychoanalytic Dialogues*, 14(4), 405–422.

Chapter 7

Racism and the psychoanalytic profession

Introduction

My first experience of a formal discussion about race and racism within the world of psychotherapy was in the 1980s when, as a trainee, I attended a presentation by Lennox Thomas in my training organisation. Lennox was one of the first black people to train in psychoanalytic psychotherapy in Britain and became an important figure as a writer, teacher and activist. Originally trained as a social worker, he went on to become Clinical Director of NAFSIYAT, the Intercultural Therapy Centre in North London which was established in 1980 by Jafar Kareem. He was Co-Director of the University College (London) MSc in Intercultural Psychotherapy and co-founder of the Refugee Therapy Centre in London. Lennox died in 2020.

The seminar I attended occurred around thirty-five years ago, but I still have memories of the evening. I came to London to train and was employed as a care worker in a therapeutic community for adults with mental health difficulties in North West London. There I met and worked with black colleagues and clients and was on a steep learning curve regarding racism – especially my own. Lennox's presentation, therefore, was very welcome. Throughout the talk Lennox was controlled and gentle, taking care not to alienate his all white, mostly female audience. He drew comparisons with gender, speaking of his obligation as a man to be aware of, and think about, the female experience and to take responsibility for how his behaviour might impact on women. He was asking us, in turn, to take responsibility for our racism. Throughout the evening, he applied a solid understanding of psychoanalytic principles to make his case.

I was impressed and moved by the talk as he opened up connections between what I was learning in my training and my experiences at work and presented a whole new landscape I was keen to explore. Eagerly I waited for the discussion to see how others were affected and what my training organisation might consider doing in response. However, the conversation was deeply disappointing. No one directly challenged Lennox. No blatantly racist comment was made. Every speaker started with gratitude and an almost obsequious praise. Then each went on to make a comment that served to eradicate any possibility of potency from his talk. There was a series of personal statements from the audience, all of which asserted an exceptionalism that removed the speaker from the list of whites who might need to think about his words. Others asked why we were not discussing other injustices (class, gender, sexuality etc.), managing to drown the matter of racism in a list of social wrongs. Further 'questions' were thinly disguised complaints that, really, it was all black people's fault.

Over years of writing and speaking on the subject I have heard the ways we white people defend ourselves from thinking about our own racism many, many times. The list is depressingly limited, ubiquitous and repetitive.

Since that evening I have tried to address the issue of racism from a number of positions within the profession, starting as the angry young trainee, to writing and teaching as a more senior member of the profession, to becoming chair of my own membership and training organisation, and then chair of my regulatory body, the British Psychoanalytic Council. Working with colleagues we conducted research projects, set up working groups and conferences, raised matters at Council and called meetings of those responsible for training.

There has been some change. I used to experience outright hostility where students and course participants were openly angry that time had to be spent on this 'irrelevant' subject when they had so many other things to learn. People now are generally more open to the chance to focus on the problem and think about the implications for themselves and their work. I do know individuals change. However, apart from some tinkering, our institutions do not.

This resistance to change finds parallels with our profession's other thorny subject – sexuality. Many of the more worrying concepts and texts which have racist or homophobic roots and implications continue to be taught without examination or even awareness of how they might be received by someone who is black or gay. There is no active prohibition now against gay people training, but worrying comments are still made referring to a failed Oedipal stage and even perversion. The process of training remains stubbornly resistant to the various creative ways that have been put forward for reducing costs, allowing a wider representation in terms of class. Research done into the experience of people from the LGBTQ community and from BAME groups shows that many find it hard to find their place in our institutions. While there are some significant LGBTQ and black and Asian colleagues who have made it through the training, many of whom have made a considerable contribution to the psychoanalytic and Jungian analytic literature, there are still very few who apply. Given the diversity of multi-cultural, twenty-first-century Britain, we are looking increasingly irrelevant.

Shannon Sullivan (2006) considers the trajectory of the great classical philosopher of race, W.E.B. Du Bois, who began with

> a 'liberal' approach to the elimination of racism. Du Bois's liberalism naively posited human beings as always wishing to do good and as failing to do so only because they did not know what the good was. . . . Calling for white people to become more familiar with the lives and situations of black people,

Du Bois put his faith in the basic goodness of white people. Their increased knowledge would reduce black people's (perceived) foreignness and eliminate the reason for white people's racist attitudes and behaviours towards them.

(p. 20)

After World War I, Du Bois went through a process of considerable disillusionment until he reached the position where he saw that

to understand the white ignorance of non-white people, one has to hear the active verb 'to ignore' at the root of the noun. What had initially seemed to him like an innocent lack of knowledge on white people's part revealed itself to be a malicious production that masked the ugly Terrible of white exploitative ownership of non-white people and cultures.

(p. 20)

I can identify a little with the naivety in believing we 'white folk' (Du Bois, 1920/2016) just needed to educate ourselves about the experience of black people, and things would change. I assumed that the profession of psychoanalytic psychotherapy would be especially open to the challenge, as at our heart is a recognition and awareness of unconscious dynamics within the psyche that have a profound effect on our thoughts and action. I assumed we would be keen to understand our hidden racism and bring our analytic skills to the table in order to address the problem. I now believe that there are aspects of our thinking and our ways of training and structuring ourselves that contrive to ensure that the idea that there *is* a problem to address is neutralised in what Bob Young (1994) describes as 'a loud silence'. This is despite the evidence that comes from those from minority ethnic communities and years of concerned members of the profession writing and speaking on the subject.

The experience of Black, Asian and Minority Ethnic trainees

People of colour who have grown up in Britain will have suffered from racism in some form or another; it will have been – and continue to be – a dimension of their personal and social life which needs acknowledgement and understanding. However, it is often reported by black psychotherapy students that their predominantly white analysts, supervisors and trainers mostly fail to recognise the reality of the problem. The consequence is, at best, significant concerns and personal experiences are not thought about and understood within the ordinary analytic endeavour, or, at worst, previous trauma is repeated and reinforced.

In 2004, Margaret James-Franklin interviewed a number of black psychoanalytic psychotherapists who had trained in different psychotherapy organisations about their experiences for her MSc dissertation. Some years later a group of us in the (then) British Association of Psychotherapists (BAP) carried out a survey across the organisation; the findings were written up by Karen Ciclitira and Nina Foster and published in 2012. In 2013/2014 the Ethnicity, Culture and Racism Task Group of the regulatory body, the British Psychoanalytic Council (BPC), chaired by Maxine Dennis, undertook a survey of BPC registrants on attitudes to how ethnicity is addressed in their Member Institution. These findings were presented to an extended meeting of the senior leadership of the training organisations which are registered with the BPC.

What emerges from this research is how hard it is for the black individual to get through a training in psychotherapy. The pressures are subtle but wearing. Some felt that their ethnicity attracted negative special attention during the interview process, citing instances of being quizzed on matters not put to white applicants. Many spoke of raising questions and concerns in seminars about theoretical and clinical material from the point of view of diversity, racial difference, cultural variation, racism, etc. which were ignored or dismissed by teachers and peers who were clearly uncomfortable in speaking freely on these issues. Many were told explicitly or implicitly that, because this was depth, analytic work, the difference in 'race' and colour was irrelevant. This leaves the black trainee in an invidious position. If they raise the issue they can be seen as being 'difficult' in bringing such uncomfortable matters into the room, or failing to be sufficiently 'analytic' by focusing on so-called outer world concerns. But if they don't speak, then they collude with what amounts to a whitewash. Very few could recall times when the subject was raised by white seminar leaders, supervisors or colleagues.

Taken as a whole, the research reveals a climate of colour blindness where trainers, supervisors and analysts take the position that differences in colour are not noticed and not relevant to in-depth, analytic work; we are assumed to all be the same. This denial of the reality of the impact of racism and power differentials means the black trainee is required to disregard important aspects of her or his experience and put aside their 'blackness' if they are to survive.

Frank Lowe (2006) is a British black psychoanalytic psychotherapist who has been writing and speaking on this subject for many years. He says:

> I haven't met a black therapist or trainee therapist who has been satisfied with their training organization's handling of race issues or feels confident that the profession is addressing the problem. I have explored how colour blindness or race avoidance can occur as a defence against fear and helplessness and I believe it also operates at an institutional level as a mechanism to maintain power, i.e. the status quo with its traditional power relations, authority and control.
>
> (p. 56)

He goes on to quote from a number of black colleagues about their experience of training:

Whenever I raise issues about race and culture, I am told this course is about the internal world not social issues.

(Trainee child psychotherapist)

During my interview I was asked about working with white patients but none of my fellow white trainees were asked about their ability to work with black patients.

(Adult psychotherapist)

I feel isolated with my experience of the training and I do not feel confident that I will get support if I talk about my experience and views as a black person. I think it's probably best to just keep my head down and get through the training.

(Black trainee adult psychotherapist)
(pp. 56–57)

Eugene Ellis is the founder and director of the Black and Asian Therapy Network (BAATN) in the UK. In an interview (2013), he points out:

What tends to happen with Black trainees is that they enter into the spirit of enquiry that is encouraged on any counselling or psychotherapy training course, but when they do so in the area of their culture and their race, there is all this silence and it's like you've just opened a huge hole in the floor. Somehow it becomes your fault. You can then choose either to say nothing, because it's too painful, and focus on just getting your qualification, or you insist that your voice is heard, get labelled as the troublemaker, and risk not making it to the end because you're worn out by the fighting. It's so sad to see this happen and I have heard this from so many Black and Asian students. It all goes on under the surface. Just naming what's going on becomes almost impossible and everyone gets defensive and blaming. It's normally the student of colour who gets the rougher end of things because that's how oppression works. What then happens is that students have to go outside their training to get what they need to develop as therapists within the profession.

(p. 16)

Demands are sometimes placed on the individual to speak for the whole BAME community, which has the consequence of submerging the personal experience into that of the group so that the individual cannot be seen, and stereotypes become the main organising principle. Psychotherapists from BAME communities are not a homogenous group in terms of background or experience. They are individuals with different cultures, histories, classes, sexualities and genders, all of which will have impacted on their experience in Britain and in their training. For the person from the marginalised communities, coping with projections and experiences relating to 'race' *and* being able to be an individual can be an ongoing battle both internally and externally. Their concern then is how to be accepted on one's own merits without others' preconceptions dominating the issue.

In a working note for a group interested in exploring matters of 'race' and equity in the profession, Andrew Cooper wrote the following:

> We think that for black and ethnic minority people the experience of racism tends to be pervasive in one form or another – but this does not mean that this is the whole of what their lives consist of! It is a dimension of personal and social experience. But a difficulty arises when they try to give voice to this aspect of their experience, because 'white' anglo-saxon people and institutions usually do not, or cannot, hear and simply take it seriously for what it is – one very important matter that needs understanding, recognition, and thought. We think the consequence of such a failure of response is predictable, and inevitable – a redoubled effort to make others 'take in' the seriousness of the issue, which can in turn lead to a more strenuous effort to renounce the (now even more) unpalatable communication. The stage is set for systematic misunderstanding and a culture of defensive 'race relations' – black people have a chip on their shoulder and white people are racist.
>
> (Internal BAP communication, July 2005)

A similar dynamic is described by Farhad Dalal (1998):

> What the marginalized groups are then forced to do, *as a strategic necessity*, is to . . . assert an essentialism at the margins – the point about being at the margins is that the centre finds it hard to hear, partly because of psychological distance, and partly because what is being said is inconvenient. And so the marginalized are forced to shout until hoarse and can end up sounding shrill.
>
> (pp. 206–207. Italics in original)

The Inquiry by Sir William Macpherson (1999) into the death of the black teenager Stephen Lawrence in 1993 in London defined institutional racism as

> the collective failure of an organisation to provide an appropriate and professional service to people because of their colour, culture or ethnic origin. It can be seen or detected in processes, attitudes and behaviour which amount to discrimination through unwitting prejudice, ignorance thoughtlessness and racist stereotyping which disadvantage minority ethnic people.
>
> (para. 6.34)

> It is incumbent on every institution to examine their policies and the outcome of their policies and practices to guard against disadvantaging any section of our communities.
>
> (para. 46.27)

The psychoanalytic establishment is part of this society and is as susceptible to institutionalised racism as any other. However, the urgency and commitment that is found in other professions such as social work, medicine, academia, etc. is markedly lacking in that of psychoanalytic psychotherapy. I don't think I have ever heard any blatantly racist statement made by a colleague – on the contrary, the language is usually of disapproval of racist dynamics within society. Most people I know are politically left of centre, many have worked in the public sector prior to training, and all express a concern for mental wellbeing throughout the population. And yet as an institution there has been remarkably little real change.

Cooper (2018) writes:

> Institutional racism is both a manifestation of organizational resistance to change and a main source of that resistance. But tackling institutional racism is about the pursuit of ordinariness, about creating conditions wherein, at a minimum, organizations fully effect the ordinariness of a multi-ethnic society.
>
> (p. 101)

Cooper goes on to point out that, within the multi-ethnic environments of today, the fact that

> one can find organizational enclaves apparently almost untouched by these changes is surely evidence of something deeper and more troubling. Almost without exception, I suggest, the major institutions of psychoanalytic psychotherapy and psychotherapy training in this country are just such enclaves.
>
> (p. 101)

I mentioned earlier that there is a general silence in this profession regarding racism and a denial that we have a problem. This is not quite true, as the matter *is* raised on an infrequent but regular basis. From time to time during gatherings of colleagues in committees, working groups, conferences, etc. someone will point out the whiteness of most if not all of the group. We all nod and agree the matter needs serious attention and there follows a discussion of what might be done. The conversation becomes increasingly desultory and fades away. Then the subject disappears from agendas altogether until, some months later, as if obeying an implicit rule, the subject will be raised again. We go round and round the same circle and effectively nothing changes. Ellis describes the response should a black person persist beyond what seems to be the allotted time allowed for debate. If a white person does so, there is far less risk, but there will be a general irritation and they are likely to be labelled – perhaps not as a troublemaker but as someone with a problem.

I cannot separate myself from this depressing procedure, having played my part many times in these institutionalised practices, but I am coming to believe that these discussions are themselves part of a complicit contract we are all engaged in to ensure against the radical change that is required. There is a sense of help-lessness that is evident in the conversation. People feel caught in a catch-22 of wanting to increase the diversity of the group and hence that of the work and the decisions made, but the pool of available black colleagues is limited, and they can't be everywhere. Besides, there are worrying questions of tokenism, of look-ing to black people to save us whilst we assume a position of helplessness.

We have plenty of evidence open and available to us, both of the experience of black people in the profession and what they believe are ways forward, in the form of research reports, papers and articles. It seems white people are unable to imagine questions we might ask ourselves, actions we might take, feelings we could explore and ways of doing so. Instead we are left in a state of apparent paralysis as if there is nothing to be done and, with apparent regret (and a sigh of relief?), we move on.

Cordial racism

In their presentation to the IAAP Congress on racism in Brazil in Cape Town, Paula Boechat and Walter Boechat (1998) quoted from a publication by a group of journalists and sociologists on their research on racism in Brazilian society (Folha de S. Paulo, 1998). They called their results 'Racismo Cordial'. This struck me as a rather apt term for the sort of racism that exists within our institutions. Cordial, but no less deadening for that.

DiAngelo (2018) notes that:

> To continue reproducing racial inequality, the system only needs white peo-ple to be really nice and carry on, smile at people of color, be friendly across race, and go to lunch together on occasions. I am not saying you shouldn't be nice. I suppose it's better than being mean. But niceness is not coura-geous. Niceness will not get racism on the table and will not keep it on the table when everyone wants it off. In fact, bringing racism to white people's attention is often seen as not nice, and being perceived as not nice triggers white fragility.
>
> (p. 153)

DiAngelo (2011) calls the usual response to this 'not nice' challenge when racism is brought to the table as *White Fragility*:

> Because White Fragility finds its support in and is a function of white privi-lege, fragility and privilege result in responses that function to restore equi-librium and return the resources 'lost' via the challenge – resistance towards the trigger, shutting down and/or tuning out, indulgence in emotional inca-pacitation such as guilt or hurt feelings, exiting, or a combination of these responses.
>
> (p. 58)

White fragility is *not* weakness but a means of maintaining the privilege of whiteness. This fragility takes the form of a sort of colour blindness that bypasses the realities of inequality and negates the need for engagement with the consequences of disparity and discrimination. This means we are unused to engaging in ordinary conversations about the fact of that privilege and its implications. We have nothing like the resilience of black friends and colleagues with whom honest engagement becomes fraught with our anxiety, defensiveness and denial.

The silence, the 'huge hole in the floor' that Ellis describes, suggests that the process of disavowal I discussed in an earlier chapter is in operation. Disavowal involves a vertical split in the psyche of the white liberal with the racist thought and the investment in white privilege on one side and a need to maintain a sense of oneself as good on the other. Between the two is a void, a silent gap, lacking the capacity for mourning or symbolisation which Adrienne Harris (2012) – borrowing from Andre Green (1970) – calls a 'psychose blanche'. Discussions around racism in the profession often have a dead feel to them, as if we are going through the motions until, lacking libidinal investment, the conversation dribbles away and we can return to things as they were. I am coming to see such familiar discussions as a form of institutional ritual that acts to patch over the gap so that it is never properly faced and worked with. It serves the dual purpose of allowing us to feel we are doing something, that we are being nice, whilst actually ensuring that nothing really changes.

A problematic history

Both the theory and method of psychoanalysis and Jungian analysis contains an exasperating polarity that makes it both profoundly radical and also deeply conservative. As Stephen Frosh (2013) puts it: 'This ambiguity inherent in psychoanalysis infects everything it comes into contact with. Both conformist and revolutionary, both racist and emancipatory, it shows how we are continuously infiltrated by things we know little about, or that we thought we had escaped' (p. 9). This ambiguity, present in the theory itself with its roots in colonial anthropology, I explored in Chapter 5. But the history of the development of the practice and organisation of psychoanalysis also holds a polarity which we inherit today.

Neil Altman (2010) references Gilman (1993) who pointed out that, at the time when Freud and his followers were working on this new theory in Vienna, Jews were thought of as 'blacks' and, therefore, psychoanalysis was thought of as a 'black thing' (p. 122). At the start, the project developed at the margins of society and spoke its radical message from this position. As Freud and his followers left Germany and Austria and moved elsewhere, they needed to fit in, find acceptance and establish a place within the privileged world of the white middle classes of the UK and the Americas. The price of this contract was the omission of race and social class from its discourse and consequently the increased homogeneity of its members such that today, looking around most gatherings of psychoanalytic psychotherapists, one could be forgiven for thinking that psycho-analysis has now become a 'white thing': 'When a black thing turns into a white thing, we might well wonder what processes of disavowal and repression are at work' (p. 122).

> As a black thing in a white society, psychoanalysis attained the power of the outsider to gain perspective to critique, to see in the dark. A large share of the value of psychoanalysis derives from the ability of Freud and his follow-ers to bring to light that which was disavowed and repressed. In becoming white in America, psychoanalysts forfeited some of that night vision, most particularly with respect to our own social (meaning racial and class) position and the ways this process might be reflected in clinical work. The position we have on the polarity is reversed, but the polarity remains. And so we find ourselves needing and resisting the critique, the psychoanalytic intervention, of those we have left out.
>
> (p. 123)

Altman's book is called *The Analyst in the Inner City*. He points out that '[h]istorically, psychoanalysis has largely eschewed concern with inner-city public clinic work. . . . Psychoanalysts concentrated on private practice, where condi-tions more neatly fitted the classical ideal and where, not incidentally, there was more money to be made' (p. xv). The British psychoanalyst Harvey Taylor (2013) in his discussion paper notes that

> at the 1918 Budapest international conference Freud and the early pioneers agreed that psychoanalysis would develop along three fronts: research, train-ing and subsidised clinics. Owing to inflation and political developments in Eastern Europe only the training option was developed, supported by a lim-ited research effort based on the case history.
>
> (pp. 2–3)

The abandonment of the subsidised clinic and of the discourse around race and class has deprived the discipline of a width of human experience and nar-rowed the field of knowledge. There are those in the psychoanalytic community who, like Altman, work in public health settings, in prisons and in working class community projects, with the homeless and the poor, and have first-hand experi-ence of the impact of social injustice and oppression on the individual and the family. Yet they have little say in the formulation of our clinical theory. We rarely hear case presentations involving shop assistants, migrant workers, lorry drivers or care workers. Jennifer Tolleson (2009), in her ironically titled paper 'Saving the World One Patient at a Time', notes that '[w]orking from the margins, these clinicians have contact with our culture's hidden subjectivities . . . [which] com-prise hidden – subjugated – knowledges that remain, sadly, outside our formidable intelligence as a profession' (pp. 201–202).

The radical potential of psychoanalysis is expressed by Harris (2012), who asserts that

> the method of psychoanalysis (a set of contaminated tools to be sure) is a commitment to looking at both what is hidden in silence and in plain sight. Psychoanalysis, at its most unflinching and courageous, allows us to maintain curiosity at the strange, fuzzy, unreasoning moments in the psyche and in the culture. In this way, psychoanalysis has the potential to be, in part, a revolutionary practice. Or to put it more modestly, psychoanalysis can be part of a radical practice of social resistance.
>
> (p. 198)

However, the conservative pull resists taking on the revolutionary implications of our understanding when it comes to developing and supporting a radical practice in relation to race. Melanie Suchet (2007) writes,

> within psychoanalysis the place of race in the construction of subjectivity has always been minimized. A curious omission given that formation of the subject is our field of study. Discussions of race today remain largely limited to an investigation of otherness when someone of a different color enters the consulting room. Further, the burden of writing about race has until very recently fallen on those with darker skins who have been trying to tell us for decades that a racialized subjectivity is crucial.
>
> (p. 868)

'Inner' and 'outer'

Our theories presume and perpetuate a division between 'inner' and 'outer', between the 'psyche' and the 'social', where the former is the proper subject for psychoanalysis. This can lead to an assumption, not always explicit, that injustices such as racism are 'outer', social world phenomena; therefore, of little or no relevance to analytic enquiry. It is true that theorising about the psychological implications of racism reach back to Fanon (1986), to Kovel (1988), and through to modern-day writers such as Brewster (2020), Dalal (2002), Davids (2011), Keval (2016), Kimbles (2000) and Lowe (2006), all of whom offer a sophisticated understanding of how racism works within the psyche and in interaction with the other. Traditionally our theories isolate the individual from their social world, and we prioritise the personal over the political although recent developments such as relational psychoanalysis seek to re-instate the link. Dalal (2001, 2002) challenges the assumptions behind the usual psychoanalytic perspectives which he sees as locating the *cause* of racism as an internal world dynamic rather than in the social world. He says: 'In my opinion, the problems thrown up in this territory shed light on a more general difficulty in psychoanalytic theories; a difficulty born of a false distinction between the *developmental* and *socialization* processes' (2002, p. 80. Italics in original).

In academia there is a debate about the validity of any division between the internal and the external and the implications of isolating one from the other. Stephen Frosh and Lisa Baraitser (2008), for example, argue that:

> The division is . . . a way of doing politics, and the psycho-social becomes a contrary way of doing politics, a rebellion that asserts that you cannot have one without the other, that they are warp and weft and signifier and signified, and so on through the different ways of saying that they are two sides of the same thing.
>
> (p. 349)

In his response to this paper, Paul Hoggett (2008) takes issue with the idea that the distinction should be dissolved entirely, asserting a belief 'that the internal and external worlds, while overlapping and mutually constituting, are also irreducible to one another. Each is governed by its own rules of structure formation' (p. 383). He goes on to argue that

> the hyphen in psycho-social signifies a difference that cannot be dissolved. It therefore opens up the space for thinking, like an enzyme that assists digestion. Individual/social dualism is not overcome by merging them, by making them simply a matter of perspective.
>
> (p. 383)

I came across this intriguing and thought-provoking debate within psycho-social studies in my research for this book. It struck me that our profession ought to be more actively involved in the conversation, both because of what we might contribute and what we could learn. It was not the first time I stumbled on a perspective from outside of the world of clinicians that challenged a set of age-old assumptions and woke up my thinking. It underlined how insulated we are from other disciplines. In our conferences, seminars and journals, we tend to talk mostly to ourselves, generally confirming or expanding slightly what we already know. It seems we are missing out on a world of thinking and debate which we might find stimulating, original and helpful, for we could do with collapsing a little the old categories of the individual and the social, the internal and the external, and find better ways of theorising how human suffering can be both personal *and* collective.

Complacency

To turn to the libraries of other specialties – even those who are our friends – requires a certain humility which I fear can be lacking in our world. Doubtless all disciplines have their certainties, but that of psychoanalytic psychotherapy seems particularly prone to complacency. There is a tendency – possibly exacerbated by external attack – towards a position of arrogance where our theories are spoken as if they were 'the truth'. Sometimes when we take psychoanalytic thinking out into society, we do so as if we bring a golden thing for which the world should be grateful. A humility is required of us, one that recognises we too have much to learn. To borrow from Bion: 'Psycho-analysis is just one stripe on the coat of the tiger' (Bion, 1991, p. 112).

Frosh and Baraitser (2008) again:

> many psychosocial researchers share the traditional sociological suspicion of psychoanalysis because of its strong individualizing tendencies, while those who have been most influenced by poststructuralist and/or discursive perspectives resist the 'top-down' expert-knowledge epistemological strategies of psychoanalysis with their apparent certainties about the 'true' nature of human subjectivity, accompanied by an interpretive practice that always seems to know best, or at least to know subjects better than they know themselves.
>
> (p. 347)

I wonder if one of the strengths of our craft – the fact that all psychoanalytic psychotherapists are required to be in analysis throughout our trainings – might also be a weakness. Perhaps there is a tendency to an unconscious – even conscious – belief in what I have come to think of as the myth of the complete analysis which leads to complacency, as if we somehow have things more or less sorted. This is particularly dangerous when talking about race. Given most white members have had analysis with a white analyst, I suspect the analysand will not have spent many sessions exploring their racism. Certainly, I don't recall the subject ever coming up in mine. Yet I am often surprised by the certainty I meet in individuals as if there really is nothing further that needs consideration or thought about oneself.

Ways forward

There are many thoughtful, socially concerned and politically aware people within the profession who are troubled by injustice and discriminatory practices and are genuine in their wish to make a difference. But we work against conscious and unconscious dynamics that operate in ourselves as individuals and in our institutions and we need to recognise and be careful of these undercurrents and their effects if we are to take on the hard work that is needed if change is to come about. I suggest the usual discussions that many will be familiar with are not only futile but are a part of the defensive structures that serve to act against the radical change that is needed. If such structures are there to defend out white privilege, then radical change will require acknowledgement of that privilege and letting it go. There will be loss and discomfort, but I argue that our liberal, justice and knowledge-seeking concerned selves will gain immeasurably.

Here are some suggestions for action. They do require a level of agreement that this is a white problem, and a commitment by individuals, groups and organisational leadership to get on with the work.

Suggested ways forward:

1 A radical review of the theories we use through a series of reading groups and group discussions. There is a paucity of material within the analytic texts that offers a thorough critique of the colonial roots of some of the terms we use and we will need to borrow heavily from those in academia such as psychosocial studies, philosophy and social work. There are colleagues in these departments who understand and are sympathetic to psychoanalytic theory but have also researched and written about the more questionable history and modern-day implications. Recently in my own organisation, the British Jungian Analytic Association (BJAA) within the BPF, groups of us have met to explore potentially troubling concepts such as the 'primitive', 'inner and outer' and the more Jungian concepts of 'animus/anima' and *'participation mystique'*. For each meeting we read two papers on the topic – usually from contrasting perspectives – and then met to discuss. Having considered the material from a mainly theoretical perspective, we then went further to explore clinical implications. According to the responses from those involved, this has led for some to an organic re-vision of these concepts and a re-think of the way we work and teach. Certainly, the energy generated has been in considerable contrast with the flat, deadly discussions we usually have about racism, gender and sexuality. I gather that the words 'critique' and 'crisis' have a common etymological origin. Certainly members of the group reported a sense a crisis of thought in this process of critiquing long accepted, previously unquestioned theories, but most seemed to feel it was a crisis worth weathering.

2 A greater vigilance regarding language and text following our 'self-education'. As I have written elsewhere (Morgan, 2019):

> The writings of our analytic forbears, sadly especially Jung, is peppered with assumptions, pronouncements and language which is ugly and abusive. . . . As a white analyst, teacher and supervisor, it is *my* responsibility to see and to question and be disturbed by the disturbing and questionable material. I need to imagine what it might feel like to have one's ancestors referred to as 'savage' or 'primitive'. . . . Either I must leave such texts off the reading list or I must introduce them in a manner that acknowledges the hurt they may cause and open up and facilitate a conversation about the implications. This must be done whether there is a black person present or not. For if we train white analysts to believe there is nothing to notice, nothing to be concerned about, then the abuse continues, and we cripple the future growth of therapists.

(pp. 356–357)

3   From an organisational perspective, each training and/or membership or regulatory body should undertake a thorough evaluation of all aspects of its life from monitoring systems, policies, structures, etc. Frank Lowe (2006) writes:

> There must be a systematic review of analytic organizations' ways of functioning, in terms of whether and how they disadvantage black and minority communities. This would include the selection of psychotherapists for training, content of training programmes and supervision arrangements. Overall, this is about changing organizational culture and developing a non-defensive but non-persecutory approach to exploring racism rather than avoidance, denial and splitting it off from awareness at the intra-psychic, interpersonal, group and organizational levels.
>
> (pp. 49–50)

4   A development of seminars, scientific meetings and conferences on how racism operates, theoretically but also as a live internal process which utilises ways familiar in the profession for deepening understanding. Group relation events also help to bypass the intellectualising defences and offer safe spaces for people to contemplate racism on a personal level. The radical/conservative binary that runs as a thread through our theory and practice also runs through us as organisations, groups and individuals. It becomes too easy to split the binary, take up one of the polarised positions and deny and disown the opposite, leading to stuckness. We might need external support and consultancy to help us with this.

Joel Kovel (1988) uses the term 'saturate' to describe the way in which racism has penetrated every corner of the society into which we are all born. There is no position one can take which is outside it. If we acknowledge the racist backdrop to our world then we also have to recognise the particular prejudicial veil which is the inheritance of all white members of this society – including psychoanalytic practitioners. The veil may well be one of cordiality, but it has guilt, shame and envy woven into it, complicated as it is by the hatred of the internal racist. It is fear of such shame which freezes our curiosity about each other and prevents us from having ordinary conversations about the reality of the external and the internal divides caused by racism.

   In the previous chapter, Sam Kimbles's concepts of the 'cultural complex' and 'phantom narratives' were introduced as offering a helpful way of thinking about how a racist system buries its way into the underground structures of communities. The racial complex within the profession of psychoanalytic psychotherapy seems to me to have a tight hold through our dissociation, disavowal and denial that we have a problem. Complexes reveal themselves by becoming activated by an event, but our silence around the subject protects it from being energised. This might happen when the active presence of 'blackness' asserts itself, but since the number of black people in the profession is disproportionately small and those who are here can be required to put that 'blackness' to one side in order to train, and since we seem to find it so hard to challenge ourselves, things stay resolutely the same.

However, there is, I believe, a developing impatience with this state of affairs and a growing number of people who are wanting to actively bring about change. We need to expose the complex, examine it and work with, alongside, under and through it in order to bring about the change that could revitalise our theories, our trainings, our clinical practice and our organisations.

James Baldwin (1998) writes:

> The history of white people has led them to a fearful, baffling place. . . . On the one hand, they can scarcely dare to open a dialogue which must, if it honest, become a personal confession – a cry for help and healing, which is, really the basis of all dialogues – and, on the other hand, the black man can scarcely dare to open a dialogue which must, if it honest, become a personal confession which, fatally, contains an accusation. And yet, if neither can do this, each of us will perish in those traps in which we have been struggling for so long.
>
> (pp. 724–725)

There is an ethical imperative for the white practitioner and the analytic institution to engage with humility and integrity in the dialogue Baldwin describes, and develop a level of resilience that can bear the pain of our confession and the accusation of the black patient or colleague. If we do not do so, then we and the analytic endeavour will perish in the trap Baldwin describes.

References

Altman, N. (2010) *The Analyst in the Inner City. Race, Class and Culture Through a Psychoanalytic Lens*. Sussex and New York: Routledge.

Baldwin, J. (1998) The White Man's Guilt. *Collected Essays*. Ed: Orison, T. New York: Library Classics (Original work published 1965).

Bion, W.R. (1991) *A Memoir of the Future*. London: Karnacs.

Boechat, P., and Boechat, W. (1998) *Racismo Cordial*. Ed: Folha de S. Paulo, Second Edn. Sao Paulo: Ática.

Brewster, F. (2020) *The Racial Complex. A Jungian Perspective on Culture and Race*. Oxon and New York: Routledge.

Ciclitira, K., and Foster, N. (2012) Attention to Culture and Diversity in Psychoanalytic Trainings. *British Journal of Psychotherapy*, 28(3), 353–373.

Cooper, A. (2018) Institutional Racism: Can Our Organizations Change? *Conjunctions. Social Work, Psychoanalysis and Society*. Oxon: Routledge.

Dalal, F. (1998) *Taking the Group Seriously: Towards a Post-Foulkesian Group Analytic Theory*. London: Jessica Kingsley Publishers.

Dalal, F. (2001) Insides and Outsides: A Review of Psychoanalytic Renderings of Difference, Racism and Prejudice. *Psychoanalytic Studies*, 3(1), 43–66.

Dalal, F. (2002) *Race, Colour and the Process of Racialization: New Perspectives from Group Analysis, Psychoanalysis and Sociology*. Hove, East Sussex: Brunner Routledge.

Davids, F. (2011) *Internal Racism: A Psychoanalytic Approach to Race and Difference.* Basingstoke: Palgrave Macmillan.

DiAngelo, R. (2011) White Fragility. *International Journal of Critical Pedagogy*, 3(3), 54–70.

DiAngelo, R. (2018) *White Fragility. Why It's So Hard for White People to Talk About Racism.* New York: Beacon Press.

Du Bois, W.E.B. (2016) The Souls of White Folk. *Darkwater. Voices from Within the Veil.* London: Verso (First published in 1920 by Harcourt, Brace and Company).

Ellis, E. (2013) Silenced: The Black Student Experience. *Therapy Today*, December. www.therapytoday.net

Fanon, F. (1986) *Black Skin, White Masks.* London: Pluto Press (First published in 1952 by Editions de Seuil).

Folha, de S. Paulo (1998) *Racismo Cordial*, Second Edn. Sao Paulo: Ática.

Frosh, S. (2013) *Hauntings: Psychoanalysis and Ghostly Transmissions.* London: Palgrave Macmillan.

Frosh, S., and Baraitser, L. (2008) Psychoanalysis and Psychosocial Studies. *Psychpoanalysis, Culture & Society*, 13, 346–365.

Gilman, S. (1993) *Freud, Race and Gender.* Princeton, NJ: Princeton University Press.

Green, A. (1970) The Dead Mother. *On Private Madness.* London: Hogarth Press.

Harris, A. (2012) The House of Difference, or White Silence. *Studies in Gender and Sexuality*, 13(3), 197–216.

Hoggett, P. (2008) What's in a Hyphen? Reconstructing Psychosocial Studies. *Psychoanalysis, Culture & Society*, 13, 379–384.

James-Franklin, M. (2004) *Processes of Adaptation in Black Trainee Therapists*, Unpublished Dissertation, MSc in the Psychodynamics of Human Development, Birkbeck College, University of London.

Keval, N. (2016) *Racist States of Mind. Understanding the Perversion of Curiosity and Concern.* London: Karnac Books Ltd.

Kimbles, S. (2000) The Cultural Complex and the Myth of Invisibility. *The Vision Thing, Myth, Politics and Psyche in the World.* London: Routledge.

Kimbles, S. (2014) *Phantom Narratives: The Unseen Contributions of Culture to Psyche.* Lanham, MD: Rowman & Littlefield.

Kovel, J. (1988) *White Racism. A Psychohistory.* London: Free Association Books.

Lowe, F. (2006) Racism as a Borderline Issue: The Avoidance and Marginalization of Race in Psychotherapy. *Difference: An Avoided Topic in Practice.* Eds: Foster et al. London: Karnac.

Macpherson, W. (1999) *The Stephen Lawrence Inquiry: Report of an Inquiry.* London: HM Stationery Office.

Morgan, H. (2019) Response to Fanny Brewster and Alan Vaughan. *Journal of Analytical Psychology*, 64(3), 349–366.

Suchet, M. (2007) Unravelling Whiteness. *Psychoanalytic Dialogues*, 17(6), 867–886.

Sullivan, S. (2006) *Revealing Whiteness. The Unconscious Habits of Racial Privilege.* Bloomington, IN: Indiana University Press.

Taylor, H. (2013) *UK Psychoanalysis: Mistaking the Part for the Whole.* British Psychoanalytic Council Discussion Paper.

Tolleson, J. (2009) Saving the World One Patient at a Time: Psychoanalysis and Social Critique. *Psychotherapy and Politics International*, 7(3), 190–205.

Young, R. (1994) Psychoanalysis and Racism: A Loud Silence. *Mental Space.* London: Process Press.

Chapter 8

Race and supervision[1]

When Sara, an Asian woman, began her psychoanalytic psychotherapist training, she joined a supervision group. The supervisor and the two other members
of her group were white. At their first group supervision session, the supervisor
asked what concerns they might have in starting work with their first patient and
Sara said she had been wondering about the possible reactions of a white patient
expecting to see a white therapist who then discovers that their new therapist
was brown. The supervisor responded by saying, 'Oh. You poor thing!' and then
moved on to the next member of the group and the matter was never raised again.
For the next year Sara's experience was of being constantly criticised and under-
mined by the supervisor – an experience corroborated by the other members of
the group. In her regular assessment reports the supervisor questioned her ability
to understand internal processes and criticised her work. Sara survived the experience by ensuring that she exposed very little of herself; she kept her head down
and did not mention any questions or concerns she might have regarding difference in colour again. Fortunately, there was a change of supervision arrangements
after a year and a new supervisor was able to help her think through how the matter of difference between herself and her patient might be used to illuminate the
transference. Regular assessments of her were positive and, having completed all
the requirements, she qualified as a psychotherapist.

This supervisor's response of apparent pity to a matter of genuine enquiry by
the supervisee served to patronise and undermine. Her failure to pursue the question openly in the group and her subsequent belittling of the supervisee to the
point where she considered leaving the training suggests that the issue of difference in 'race' and colour was a problem for the supervisor but was made to be that
of the supervisee. There was no overt racist comment as such, but the combination
of the supervisor's 'pity' for Sara and the consequent ignoring of the issue was a
more subtle, but no less damaging, response. Sara was not asking for sympathy;
she was asking for help in thinking about how she might work with potentially
difficult transference material. Her experience of supervision was bruising and
may well have meant an able psychotherapist turning away from the profession. If
she had, the problem would have been seen as hers and the status quo reinforced.

In all supervisory relationships the conscious and unconscious dynamics concerning exposure, shame, judgement, etc. will be present to a greater or lesser extent. Power differentials will exist especially when the supervision is set within a training whereby the supervisor's view will substantially impact on the supervisee's career. When differences in race and colour exist within the triad of supervisor, supervisee and patient, then an additional layer enters the relationship. This layer will include the unconscious dynamics of power, guilt, shame, envy and fear. Being irrational and unwanted, these are difficult matters to think about and discuss and, consequently, they are often disavowed. If the white supervisor does not allow the possibility that they might have racist thoughts, then the consequences for the supervisee or patient of colour may well be destructive.

Like all other matters of significance for an individual patient and for the therapeutic relationship, there is a need for a supervisory space that is safe, within which thinking and exploration can take place. If the space is consumed with fear and anxiety, then there will be little possibility of genuine receptivity and reflection.

There are black therapists who have written on the matter of racism in psychotherapy and who make reference to their experience as black supervisors (Dalal, 2002; Davids, 1998; Evans Holmes, 1992; Thomas, 1992). In this chapter I consider the matter from the perspective of a white supervisor which, as a white person, is the only position I have any authority from which to speak.

When I first started researching the matter of how differences in 'race', colour and culture might affect the work of supervision, I was interested to note that, apart from those black psychotherapists mentioned earlier, I could find no mention of the topic in the books I read on supervision in psychoanalytic or Jungian analytic psychotherapy. This was in stark contrast to the modern texts on supervision in counselling and social work where at least one chapter on the issue seemed always to be included. However, on reading some of those chapters in the counselling supervision books, I found the majority to take a position of cultural relativism and, in my view, they failed to address how the dynamics of race and racism can be understood from the perspective of their impact on the internal world of the psyche and on the transferential relationship. It seemed that the deeper the analytic enterprise, the less the subject is considered of relevance, until it is ignored completely in the analytic texts.

In Chapter 1, 'Whiteness', I referred to Dalal's (2002) experience as a black therapist in supervision:

> I was speaking about the theme of colour when my clinical supervisor (white) said that he was not usually aware of the person's 'race' or colour in a session; it was not a significant issue for him. This surprised me as I am often conscious in groups, and in one to one situations, of my colour in relation to others.
>
> (p. 219)

Dalal goes on to ask why he might be more sensitive than his supervisor on this matter and suggests that one can take an internalist position which would search for the cause inside of him:

> Thus it might be suggested that I am overly sensitive or have a chip on my shoulder. In effect this is an interpretation of paranoia in which I am project-ing some internal difficulty into the territory of black and white, which is now thought of as an expression of this latent difficulty.
>
> (p. 219)

By stating that he was not aware of a person's race, Dalal's supervisor was implying that there was nothing objective and external of which to be aware. Thus, by raising the issue, Dalal could be seen as presenting indications of an internal difficulty and the intimations of a paranoid state. Given the anxiety for any trainee, this semi-conscious implication by the white supervisor of 'internal difficulties' in the black supervisee must be hard to manage. Instead of the subject being open for thought, the report of black trainees is that they respond by keep-ing their heads down and learning not to mention the subject again. Some may well leave the training. Either way, the profession loses a significant voice and the potential development of the theoretical model that is being taught.

Dalal offers an alternative understanding this difference in perspective:

> The white, by virtue of their colour, is in the mainstream and near the centre, whilst the black is marginalized and nearer the edge. The closer one is to the edge, with the resultant danger of going over, the more one is aware of the circumstances that put one there – colour. Meanwhile, those at the centre have a vested interest (often unconscious) in maintaining the status quo by blanking out the colour dynamic altogether: if it does not exist in the first place then it cannot be changed. Thus, the difference between the feelings elicited in me and my supervisor are not just because of our asocial histories, but to do with where we are located in the field of power relations.
>
> (p. 219)

In a paper on multi-cultural issues and the supervision process, Angus Igwe (2003) uses a concept which I gather is familiar in professional education. Put-ting aside the fact that the word 'unconscious' is used differently from a psycho-analytic perspective, and acknowledging that the model is somewhat simplistic, it is useful when thinking about difference in the supervisory relationship. He suggests that the learning of any skill or craft moves through the following states:

1   Unconscious Incompetence (I don't know what I don't know)
2   Conscious Incompetence (I know what I don't know)

3   Conscious Competence (I know what I know)
4   Unconscious Competence (I don't know what I know)

(p. 217)

With regard to most aspects relating to clinical work, we would expect the supervisor to be at the stage of either conscious or unconscious competence, whereas
the supervisee, especially at the start of their training, may be more in the phase
of conscious or even unconscious incompetence. However, when someone white
is supervising someone black, the latter is likely to be far more aware of issues
relating to being at the margins and thus be more 'knowing' regarding issues of
race and racism. The white supervisor, dwelling as they do at the centre in Dalal's
description, is more likely to have 'blanked out the colour dynamic altogether'.
Thus, we have a reversal of the expected situation where the supervisee is more
aware, more knowing, more 'competent' than the supervisor.

Superficially, stage four, 'unconscious competence', looks very much like
stage one, 'unconscious incompetence'. The white supervisor can assume that
there is nothing to be explored within themselves, nothing interior to be analysed,
no problem of difference since difference is ignored. Any problem in the relationship that surfaces belongs, therefore, to the black other. Should the supervisor be
in a state of 'unconscious incompetence', regarding his or her internal racism,
for the supervisory pair to develop and for learning for both to take place, the
supervisor needs at least to be able to move to stage two and to become aware
that, on this matter, they do not 'know'. Even this apparently small move is not
easy. Any racist feelings may be rejected from a need to maintain a benign sense
of self. If the internal racist organisation is denied, it cannot be confronted. Add
to this a power dynamic inevitable in any supervisory relationship, and the pressure to sustain the place of 'knowing' is considerable. If this is not struggled with
by the supervisor, then the 'unconscious incompetence' becomes projected onto
either the black supervisee or the black patient. By perceiving the failure to be in
the other, the internal racist remains unchallenged and this organisation within the
supervisor's mind is reinforced.

Disavowal

In Chapter 4, 'The disavowal of whiteness', I suggested that the concept of disavowal was useful in understanding how racism operates in the mind of the white
liberal. Unlike repression, this entails a vertical split in the ego which serves to
separate the investment in white privilege and the racist thought on the one side
from the condemnation and rejection of racism and the need to maintain a sense
of oneself as a 'good' person on the other. I also proposed that, in racism, there is
a gap between the two vertical layers – a silent, empty place devoid of symbols in
which it is impossible to play or grieve. I quoted Adrienne Harris (2012), who bor-
rows the concept of 'psychose blanche' from Andre Green (1970), to describe an

aspect of whiteness: 'Deeper than depression, deeper than rage, there is a blankness, a place where there is not sufficient structure for mourning, where the psyche gives way' (p. 207).

The white therapist working with a black patient can fall into this place of paralysis when faced with the patient's criticisms and challenges over the subject of racism. Because of the silence of the gap and the impossibility of thought and symbolisation, the therapist can become frozen and reactive. The role of supervision, then, is to provide a container away from the frost (and potential heat) of the moment, within which there can be a return to thinking and symbolic play. Often the recounting of the incident can itself put the supervisee back into a place of anxiety and shame, and if they are to be helped and the therapy is to progress, then there needs to be trust that these difficult matters can be talked and thought about. This means that the supervisor themselves must be able to face and work with their own internal racist structures if they are to be of help.

A white therapist and a black patient

The following example is taken from work with a white supervisee whose patient, Alan, is a man in his 40s who was born in the Caribbean. When he was 6 years old his parents came to Britain to find work and Alan was looked after by his grandmother and two aunts in the Caribbean. Whilst there were constant phone calls and letters from his parents, because of the costs of travel he did not see them again till he was sent for at age 13. Alan did well at school and further education and was now a successful and well-respected businessman.

As the therapy progressed, Alan experienced any feelings of dependency on his therapist as difficult. He always seemed to have good things to replace any breaks in the therapy, so it was never missed. The session we were discussing in supervision referred to the first one after a three-week break. Alan was recounting what he had done while the therapist was away – which included a consultation with an astrologist, visiting an alternative practitioner and reading several self-help psychology books – all of which he praised enthusiastically. The therapist made the interpretation that he was telling her how well he had done without her and how others had replaced her so she wasn't missed because it was hard to acknowledge how abandoned he had felt. She then linked this to being left by his parents when he was young, and the replacement of his mother by his grandmother and aunts. Alan became angry, pointing out that what had happened to him was very common amongst his generation in the Caribbean, and that it was the failure of the therapist to understand his culture that had led her to interpret it as a problem for him.

Under this attack, the supervisee abandoned her initial thoughts and her thinking became paralysed. For the moment she was no longer the therapist trying to make sense of her patient's inner world, as his spoken accusations matched her anxiety that she could be identified with the abusive coloniser. It is certainly true that socio-political imbalances globally resulting from colonisation and slavery has meant large numbers of people migrating to the colonial nation to seek work and a better life, and having to leave behind young families to the care of family elders. Nevertheless, the fact that this was perfectly understandable and on a large scale, and that the individual was well cared for by known and loved relatives, does not mean that there is no loss for the individual child, or that the surfacing of internal, unconscious consequences in the transference cannot be interpreted. It was as if the therapist feared that if she stayed in the analytic space and considered the interpretation in the usual analytic light, she would be seen to be pathologising a whole people and an entire generation. She moved instead to the apparent safety of anthropology and thus lost the task of the analytic work.

At that moment of paralysis, I believe the therapist suddenly found herself in the gap, the 'psychose blanche' of disavowal. It is certainly possible that there might be racist assumptions entwined with her analytic thinking, and these needed careful thought and examination. But this was more like panic. She feared something bad in her had been exposed, and this created an unthinkable sense of anxiety and shame. For that moment she 'lost her mind' and hence her analytic authority.

For the therapist to stay with her interpretation and then to make sense of Alan's response, she was required to hear his raising of the matter of difference, his need to assert that he was not alone and his anxiety that there might be a problem of understanding between them. What looked like respect of the view of the 'other' was, in fact, a failure to face the underlying questions raised by 'otherness', and a desertion of the analytic responsibility to the inner world of the patient. The dynamic behind this abandonment of the analytic endeavour was the arousal of the therapist's fear of her own racism and hence of feelings of shame and guilt. Ironically, of course, the consequence for the black patient was that he would receive second-rate therapy.

The case described is similar to one cited by Davids (1998), which prompts the following comments:

> please note how easy it is for one, in an apparent attempt to keep an open mind, to embark on a road that leads inevitably, I think, to a position of cultural relativism that is clinically sterile. . . . The problem of ignoring the patient's cultural background is not so much due to defective theory as a to a reluctance on the part of the analyst to acknowledge the patient's difference, which in turn reflects a fear of entering the domain of internal racism – both analyst's and patient's – within the treatment situation. Providing one is willing to enter this terrain, I find that existing psychoanalytic theories are perfectly adequate for work with the culturally different.
>
> (p. 7)

This view is echoed by Thomas (1992) in his paper on 'Racism and Psychotherapy' where he gives the example of a white supervisee who has a black patient who 'suffered at the hands of a tyrannical mother who totally dominated him and still attempts to do so' (p. 138). He discussed the point where a good working relationship is established with the therapist and, whilst recognising what he has suffered as a child, still wishes to protect his mother from 'his wish to retaliate and attack' (p. 138). He moves to a new job where his immediate boss is overtly racist and abusive. The patient brings the pain of this to his therapy, but his therapist is immobilised. She reports that 'she feels paralysed and totally useless, not knowing how she can help him. She feels that his problems are real, external, and that there is nothing she can do in therapy' (p. 138).

Thomas makes the important statement that:

> Here, it is difficult for the therapist to recognise that the unconscious does not distinguish between colour as far as the perpetrators of pain are concerned, and that in this case it was the some of the pain suffered at the hands of his mother that was now resurrected. This connection did cross her mind, but she feared using it as a bridge for an interpretation: her patient's dilemma at work, she considered, must be a separate matter. She could not see that, for her it was a separate matter, while for the patient, still the child in pain, there was not such a distinction, only repetition. Of course, making the link was not going to be easy, but it had to be made.
>
> (p. 138)

The negative transference is never easy to manage and helping the supervisee work with it is central to the work of supervision. For to avoid the negative material that is in the transference is to avoid critical features of the analysand's inner world. A crucial aspect of the supervisor's role is to use his or her countertransference to shed some light on these darker, more hidden shadow states. The fear of shame and guilt means that when there are differences in colour between the participants, even greater unconscious effort is employed in the defence against the acknowledgement of the racist thought.

According to the analytic literature, the racist thought is itself a defence – essentially of splitting and projection. By avoiding the issue, not only do we avoid the 'bad' thought we do not wish to own, but we also miss a deeper conflict that the racist thought is a defence against. The negative influence of racist responses can be thought about not just as difficulties which the black therapist needs to manage (or defend herself against), but as a potentially useful and important route into transference material.

Dorothy Evans Holmes (1992) writes of the ways that references to race can give access to transference reactions in the therapeutic situation. In the following extract she refers to an earlier (1985) paper of hers:

> 'Often it is said that patients' racist remarks in therapy constitute a defensive shift away from more important underlying conflict and that the therapist should interpret the remarks as defence and resistance'. Whilst it is the therapist's ultimate aim to help the patient understand the protective uses of defences, this aim can best be achieved *only after* the defences are elaborated.
>
> (p. 3. Italics in original)

However, this can be hard for a black therapist to manage and the supervision needs to be an open and safe space in which these dynamics can be explored.

A black therapist and a white patient

When a black supervisee is working with a white patient, it is likely that the racist defences for the patient will take subtle and secret forms. Because of the shame and guilt attached to these responses, the patient will work hard to keep such feelings from surfacing openly in the room, and indeed they are likely to be swiftly repressed even as they surface in the mind

A black member of a supervision group was working with a white man, James. James, whilst insisting that the therapy was very helpful to him, was consistently late and missed sessions from time to time. The therapist frequently reported feeling irritated and despairing in her counter-transference, and when he began saying that maybe it was time to end therapy, she recognised her own wish for him to leave. During the reporting of a session I found myself wondering whether this therapist was able to do the work and I had the thought that another (white) member of the group would have been a better 'fit' for this patient, and that she would have provided a safer container for him. Behind these thoughts was a sense of disparagement of the therapist. I was seeing the therapist as inferior and not up to the job and that this therapeutic pairing would not be able to work.

Initially when James started his therapy, the matter of differences between them was raised and he was keen to assure his therapist that this was no problem for him. Unless the racist defences are open and conscious (in which case a white patient is unlikely to start therapy with a black therapist in the first place), anything but this denial of a problem is unlikely. But conscious denial does not mean that something does not exist. There may be an idealisation and/or a disparagement of the blackness of the therapist. Guilt, shame and the rejection of shadow aspects result in the attempt to turn away from and to disown such disagreeable, 'bad' feelings and thoughts.

What the white supervisor may be able to offer here is a recognition through identification of the patient's situation. In the supervision session, my own counter-transference reactions needed to be understood as mirroring the contempt of the patient. It was the therapist who was no good. She needed to be got rid of by lateness, missed sessions and eventually giving up altogether. My thought that she was inadequate as a therapist was a clue that there was a projection of these unwanted aspects onto her. If I could convince myself that the problem was her and not my hated and hateful feelings, then she could be rejected, and I would be relieved of feeling badly.

On writing earlier on disavowal, I referred to the work of Arnold Goldberg (1999). He suggests that the challenge to the therapist when faced with vertical forms of splitting is always considerable, for the work of integration requires movement both vertically to unconscious material and horizontally across the disavowed aspects. However, it is especially difficult when there is a split in the therapist that matches that of the patient. In this case the match was between James and me, the white supervisor. There were racist elements to the way we both regarded the therapist as not good enough, but we also shared the white liberal rejection of such views and the need to keep them hidden and so maintain a sense of goodness. It was as if dormant racist thoughts and feelings were stirred up by the very fact of the existence of the black 'other', challenging a benign sense of self. If, therefore, she can be got rid of, then we can be relieved of our hateful feelings and return to the more comfortable sense of ourselves as good, caring liberal beings.

By thinking this through in the group discussion, we began to see that James's dismissal of the therapist and of the work could be seen as his need to disparage her as a black woman, and that this hid a deeper internal conflict. The disparagement and the racist defence needed elaborating before that underlying conflict could be brought to light. In the next session the therapist made an interpretation along the lines we had discussed. Not unexpectedly, James replied that there was no problem, that her being black was fine with him, was she accusing him of being racist, etc. The next session he phoned and cancelled. However, he arrived visibly shaken to the following session. He had started out late and had to run for the bus, but as he reached the bus stop, the driver – who was black – despite having seen James coming, closed the doors and pulled away from the bus stop. James 'lost it' and began yelling at the bus, shouting at the driver. What shook him in was the raw, ugly, racist nature of the insults he heard himself shouting.

At first James found it difficult to speak about this incident to his therapist and was clearly overcome with shame at what he had said. The therapist was able to work with him to surface these feelings and to gather them into the transference. His embarrassment was excruciating but, seeing that his therapist was able to withstand these disparaging, attacking thoughts that were now in the room between them, he gradually was able to allow them to exist. Complex transference material began to emerge concerning his experience of a depressed mother who was constantly despised and belittled by his father and by whom he felt abandoned. Hiding behind his need to hold his therapist as inferior were his own feelings of worthlessness and self-denigration.

None of this is straightforward, of course. Aspects of James's contempt for his therapist related to gender rather than 'race', and we do not know how he might have been with a black male therapist. The point, perhaps, is that we are not blank screens, as certain facts concerning gender, age, 'race', etc. are clearly visible to each other. Each of the members of the supervisory triad brings with them social connections as well as internal dynamics which will affect their responses to what is seen of the other. What is seen includes the colour of the other, and whether that is perceived as the same as ours or different will inevitably 'colour' our responses, both consciously and unconsciously.

In this example, when the therapist reported the words James had shouted at the bus driver in the supervision group, the violence, vilification and hatred held in the language he used was hard to hear. Hard because it spoke not only of James's deep unconscious racism, but also because it held echoes of our own. Shame and guilt usually kept them well below the surface, patched over with colour blind-ness and liberal cordiality. The words the therapist reported spelt out a primal fear of, and attack on, the 'shitty' other. It took a lot of work for the whole group, including myself, to stay with and to think and talk about what had been surfaced through James's words, but I believe by doing so, it deepened our understanding and promoted a degree of resilience in talking about racism, the absence of which is such a feature of white fragility (DiAngelo, 2018).

Assessment

Assessing the analytic capacities of any supervisee and being able to challenge inadequacies where they are observed is an important responsibility for the super-visor or trainer. This can become additionally complicated when there are differ-ences of ethnicity and culture between supervisor and supervisee.

Such complexities may include the following possibilities:

- As with any trainee, the black supervisee may indeed be struggling and, in extreme cases, need help in realising that he or she is not really fitted to analytic work. The fear of our own racism can lead the white supervisor away from properly commenting on and challenging the failings in the black trainee and thus to offer appropriate support. This is a way of abandoning the therapist, leaving them floundering and unable to either progress or to leave the training.
- Or it may be that the trainee is well able to work analytically but has identified with the patient's negative projections. The supervisor's role is then to help the supervisee recognise, understand and work with this dynamic.
- Or it might also be the case that the supervisor is unable to surface and con-front their own sense of superiority and contempt and their unconscious sense of incapacity when faced with issues of racism. Recognising and acknowl-edging one's own racist thoughts is hard, as these disrupt the benign sense of ourselves which we wish to maintain. Such thoughts and emotions often hide behind what appears to be proper clinical assessment of a supervisee as inadequate, when in fact a process of projective identification is taking place whereby the uncertainty and anxiety is having to be held by the black indi-vidual, who can then be got rid of.

The supervisor needs to be alert to the possibility that any one or all of these dynamics may be operating at any time. As with all analytic supervision, exami-nation of counter-transference responses, careful thought and open discussion with the supervisee, but also with colleagues, where necessary, are essential.

Being white, I am only able to write here from that perspective and limitations of space have meant I have only been able to focus on a couple of the permuta-tions possible within that triad. Other dynamics may well arise when both the supervisee and the patient are black. The term 'black' includes an almost infinite variety of identities and complex dynamics may emerge when, for example, an Asian therapist is working with an African Caribbean patient and the supervisor is white British. The combination that is very rarely spoken of is when all three, the supervisor, the supervisee and the patient, are white. If we follow the analytic assumption that racist thoughts are defences, then they need to be worked with like all other defences. I suspect that they are often unnoticed within this particular triad and it is more likely that they will be reinforced by assumptions, such as seeing black figures in dreams as negative symbols.

When patient, therapist and supervisor are all white

Those from a minority culture living within a majority culture which is different from their own will be more conscious of their ethnicity and may have to think about the nature of their cultural assumptions. It is easier for the majority group to take certain premises for granted and not notice, acknowledge or question their particular cultural norms and the impact these may have on others and on their own internal worlds.

With greater movement of individuals between countries, a considerable variety of patients are entering our consulting rooms from a wide range of nationalities, religions and cultures. In many cases their mother tongues will be different from our own. The patient may not be visibly different from us, but there is likely to be considerable differences between us in our expectations, norms, values and understandings. We are therapists and not anthropologists, and we are not required to read up on a patient's culture in order to 'understand' them, as if such a position would really be possible or desirable. What matters is that we are open to hear what different cultural artefacts mean for that particular individual, what their relationship is to them and how they may be impacting on the structure of their internal world.

In order to do this fully, we have to recognise that we carry into the encounter with the 'other' our own cultural 'baggage' – certain assumptions and customs inherited from our family and society – which will have unconsciously affected how we view ourselves and the world. We need to be able to recognise that our norms are just that – one set of customs and values alongside many other, equally valid sets – in order to listen to the patients and hear and respect their experience.

Of course, these ethnic, cultural and religious sets of norms are rarely neutral in relation to one another and powerful fantasies about each other may reverberate between individuals from different cultures at a profound level, even where the difference is not a visible one. The therapeutic relationship between a Jewish woman and a German man will hold within it painful historic assumptions and is likely to include shame, fear and anxiety. Or, given the Islamophobia within current British society, the analytic couple of a Muslim and a Christian will inevitably contain currents of prejudice running through it. We need to be open to recognise when such forces are at play and they will need to surface, be rearticulated and worked through.

Whilst it is important to recognise the impact of the generalities of ethnicity, culture and religion, we also need to prioritise the individual and be open to learning what their particular relationships to those generalities are. Indeed, when a white, middle class, middle aged female therapist works with a white, middle class, middle aged female patient, there may be a danger that the therapist makes assumptions that she knows and understands her patient's culture and fails to grasp the specific vicissitudes for that particular individual.

On the one hand, this whole matter is extremely complex and difficult to explore. On the other it's really quite simple, as long as one is able to stay within the analytic frame. It is colour blindness and fear of shame and guilt that results in disavowal and takes the supervisor away from our task of working with the supervisee within that frame. For the effects of 'race' and colour within the supervisory triad to be worked with as an ordinary aspect of analytic work, the internal racist has to be faced. The fact of difference has to be remembered in order that it can be forgotten.

Note

1 A version of this paper was first published as Morgan, H. (2007) The Effects of Difference of 'Race' and Colour in Supervision. *On Supervision. Psychoanalytic and Jungian Analytic Perspectives.* Eds: Petts, A., and Shapley, B. London: Karnac.

References

Dalal, F. (2002) *Race, Colour and the Processes of Racialization: New Perspectives from Group Analysis, Psychoanalysis and Sociology.* London: Brunner-Routledge.

Davids, F. (1998) *The Lionel Monteith Lecture, Lincoln Centre & Clinic for Psychotherapy,* Unpublished.

Evans Holmes, D. (1992) Race and Transference in Psychoanalysis and Psychotherapy. *International Journal of Psychoanalysis,* 73(1), 1–11.

Goldberg, A. (1999) *Being in Two Minds: The Vertical Split in Psychoanalysis and Psychotherapy.* Hillsdale, NJ: The Analytic Press.

Green, A. (1970) The Dead Mother. *On Private Madness.* London: Hogarth Press.

Harris, A. (2012) The House of Difference, or White Silence. *Studies in Gender and Sexuality,* 13(3), 197–216.

Igwe, A. (2003) The Impact of Multi-cultural Issues on the Supervision Process. *Working Inter-Culturally in Counselling Settings.* Ed: Dupont-Joshua, A. London: Brunner-Routledge.

Morgan, H. (2007) The Effects of Difference of 'Race' and Colour in Supervision. *On Supervision. Psychoanalytic and Jungian Analytic Perspectives.* Eds: Petts, A., and Shapley, B. London: Karnac.

Thomas, L. (1992) Racism and Psychotherapy: Working with Racism in the Consulting Room – An Analytic View. *Intercultural Therapy.* Eds: Kareem, J., and Littlewood, R. Oxford: Blackwood Scientific Publications.

Epilogue
The work of whiteness

For white Christians, the Bible story that justified the slave trade and placed the blame on Africans for their plight was that of Noah's son Ham who, failing to cover his eyes, saw his father naked and drunk. As a punishment he and his descendants were cursed and 'blackened' by Noah and thus were all future generations of Ham's line condemned to serve the white children of the 'good son', Japheth.

I came across an alternative African narrative (Boyd, 1991) on the origins of difference: 'All men were originally black. But when Cain killed his brother, Abel, and God shouted at him, Cain was so frightened that he turned white and his features shrunk up, making him the first white man' (p. 15).

Perhaps this tale of fratricide, murder, God's wrath and Cain's guilt offers a more fitting metaphor for what whiteness has done to people of colour down the centuries.

The video of the white policeman kneeling on the neck of George Floyd in Minneapolis on May 25, 2020, for eight minutes and forty-six seconds whilst Floyd begged for breath is shocking and deeply distressing. There was something about the intimacy of the act, the direct bodily contact, which held echoes of the violence of slavery. This was not a shooting at a distance; it involved no modern technology; it was a physical engagement that could have taken place at any time in the history of human combat. Yet this was no fair fight. All the power was with the white officers and Floyd could only appeal to their humanity, which was tragically absent at that moment. Nor is the scene one of passion involving anger or fear on the part of the police, who seem eerily calm. All the emotion is in Floyd as he desperately asserts, over and over, 'I can't breathe'. For the officer, as well as the policemen who looked on, the scene has that peculiar combination of dissociation and violence that Adrienne Harris (2019) describes.

Rabbi Abraham Joshua Heschel reminds us that 'in a free society, some are guilty, but all are responsible'. Watching that video, the question of my responsibility is raised and stays with me like a haunting. I understand why so many people of all colours joined the Black Lives Matter protests on streets across the world. The details of this particular murder – one among so many – made it especially disturbing in its raw evocation of the brutality of the slave master. Here was

Cain killing his brother all over again, and the response 'Enough!' reverberated across our nations.

But more than protest is required. The work of dismantling 'whiteness' requires far, far more than marching and toppling monuments to a loathsome aspect of our history – necessary as these acts are. There is work to be done and it requires commitment and doggedness to continue to address the matter of our casual racism and disassemble our privilege. Alongside the necessary political activity, we also need to find spaces inside ourselves and with others for enquiry. Sometimes people talk of the fear that such spaces will be 'unsafe', but I think for white people what we really mean is that they will be uncomfortable.

Adrienne Harris (2019) writes:

> What is ironic and infuriating to many contemporary people of color writing about racism is that the revelations and analysis of continuing racism by people of color is not leading to work within the white community. I use the word 'work' deliberately to mean the hard but necessary intellectual and emotional labor that will be essential to transform and unpack racism as it is lived and enacted among white persons. This is a way of suggesting that reparations, forgiveness, work across racial lines requires first work within white communities and individuals.
>
> (p. 311)

This is not easy work. Writing in the *Guardian* (2020) a couple of months after the death of George Floyd, Nesrine Malik notes how quickly '[t]he wheels of the Black Lives Matter movement are already starting to get stuck in the mire of doubt and suspicion'. She notes:

> Before protest there is oppression, lack of popular support, and the hard work of awareness-raising. After that comes the high-octane action. The moral clarity – and allies hop on board. But once the first blood rush of protests subsides, the people who are still on the streets are mocked by their erstwhile allies, impatient to find fault with the movement and get back to their lives without any further disruption.
>
> Part of the reason for their belated reluctance is that the course of actual change is unflashy. After the first moment passes, the supportive ally has nothing to show for their continued backing for the cause: there are no public high-fives for your continuing solidarity. You can't post it, you can't hashtag it; most of the time you can't even do it without jeopardising something, whether it's your income, status, job prospects or even friendships.
>
> But the main reason for the ebbing support is that change is just hard. If it wasn't the long arc of history that allegedly bends towards justice would be a very short one. And change is supposed to be hard. It is supposed to be political.

The wake

Christina Sharpe's (2016) powerfully moving book *In the Wake. On Blackness and Being* considers three meanings of the word 'wake':

1   'The track left on the water's surface by a ship; the disturbance caused by a body swimming or moved, in water; it is the air currents behind a body in flight; a region of disturbed flow' (p. 3).
2   'A watch or vigil held beside the body of someone who has died, sometimes accompanied by ritual observances including eating and drinking' (p. 10).
3   'The state of wakefulness; consciousness' (p. 4).

Weaving in her personal history with film, photography and art, she uses these meanings as a contemplation of how black people live with the aftermath of slavery and the racism of the modern world.

Sharpe considers the wake that was created as the slave ship journeyed from Africa to the Americas, and the impunity with which enslaved Africans who were ill or weak or rebellious were thrown overboard. This was a frequent occurrence but, as James Walvin (2007) puts it:

> In the prolonged history of collective suffering which formed the story of the Atlantic slave trading, few incidents compare to those of the Zong case of 1781. Luke Collingwood, captain of the Liverpool ship had 133 slaves thrown overboard to their death when supplies were running short, hoping to claim for their deaths on the ship's insurance. The case came to court in London two years later, not for mass murder but as a disputed insurance claim.
>
> (p. 86)

Sharpe (2016) also highlights this occurrence as a grim example of how black African bodies literally died in the wake of the slave ships, but she also uses the concept as a metaphor for the consideration of the suffering of black people who live their lives in the wake of the trade. Recovery requires mourning and what she calls 'wake work'. She says:

> If . . . we think of the metaphor of the wake in the entirety of its meanings (the keeping watch with the dead, the path of a ship, in the line of flight and/ or sight, awakening and consciousness) and we join the wake with work in order that we might make the wake and *wake work* our analytic, we might continue to imagine to live in the wake of slavery, in slavery's afterlives, to survive (and more) the afterlife of property.
>
> (pp. 17–18. Italics in original)

Sharpe, of course, is concerned with the disturbance that follows the centuries of slavery for black people living today. But reading this impressive work, I found myself wondering if and how the concept might apply to whiteness. Our relationship to this painful history is very different and so, therefore, is the work. We who are descendants of the white people who sailed those ships, who invested in the trade, who profited from the trade – that is to say all white people – need also to address our past. The whiteness of the waves created by the ships soon disappear, the waters close over the black African bodies and flat calm is restored. For the white bystander, no permanent *visible* scar remains. The ships may have passed but without justice, without reparation, without collective grieving and the eradication of racism, the trauma of those times continues to be held in the generations of black descendants just as it was inflicted so brutally on George Floyd. White ancestral history, the role of the perpetrators, the impact on the victims as well as the extent to which we profited and continue to profit, demands recognition. This history should be central to the curriculum taught to all our children but, for those of us whose education touched only lightly on the matter, it is our responsibility to educate ourselves now as adults.

It is shameful that we have allowed statues to slavers such as Edward Colston to dominate our public spaces for so long, failed to erect monuments to those who were enslaved and consistently avoid addressing the matter of reparation. Black bodies were subjugated, imprisoned, abused and murdered in order that white ones could prosper. The very least we owe those who suffered so is the dignity of recognition.

The second meaning of the term 'wake' refers to its place in the process of mourning. We keep watch with the dead and grieve their passing. A wake is traditionally a collective activity which acknowledges that the death of one affects the whole. These are essential communal rituals especially when a death is the result of a collective failure, for without them the undigested, un-mourned suffering of previous generations are passed down from generation to generation as phantom narratives that pervade our personal and social lives.

For black people who are the direct descendants of the enslaved, the grief is direct. The idea that white people too need to grieve might seem odd given that we have gained so much and apparently lost so little in the history of race. Yet there are myths which have sustained us for centuries that we need to let go and bury. Peggy McIntosh (1989) describes white insistence on maintaining the notion that all is now fair and equal in our modern cultures as the 'myth of meritocracy', despite the overwhelming evidence that this is clearly not so in just about every corner of our society from education to the arts, from health to criminal justice. As we study and explore the privilege of white skin, such a myth fades to nothing. As we face the guilt of whiteness past and present, we have to let go the myth of our white innocence and purity and acknowledge the darkness at its heart. The privilege paid for by the blood of others has a toxicity at its root which corrupts the psyche. Terrible damage has been done and will continue to be done if we are to go on basing our economic and political ways of being on racist structures. Only by facing the pain and the guilt of the ancestors and of our inheritance, only by keeping vigil, can we come anywhere near to laying the iniquities of slavery to rest.

Such work brings us to the third meaning of the term 'wake', which is to 'wake up' to the way the world is structured and to our personal part in it. For white people this means a lifelong process of active commitment to examine and confront both internal and external activities that are based in prejudice and stereotypes which depersonalise and do harm to the black other. It demands a careful attention to the thoughts and responses that arrive in the mind, not so they might be banished, but because their exploration will help us see how the system of racism within which we live expresses itself in our minds.

As Harris (2012) puts it:

> To turn to a deconstruction of whiteness is to make the unremarkable remarkable, to force unexamined assumptions, to open up a set of questions. The goal, of course, is to see whiteness as a social construction, to see that whiteness is the unmarked category and in that particular way accrues and hoards power. This kind of analysis is intended to undermine both the category itself and the psychic and cultural work the category of whiteness does.
>
> (p. 200)

Because this system is biased in our favour and privileges us, because part of that privilege is the invisibility of our whiteness, taking on this work requires us to make active, determined and ongoing choices. The fragility in whiteness that maintains that privilege keeps pulling us away from the discomfort that is inevitable if we are to fully engage in that exploration. We are required to build a stamina and a resilience in speaking about the subject if we are to genuinely support anti-racist activities. DiAngelo (2018) puts it thus: 'To increase the racial stamina that counters white fragility, we must reflect on the whole of our identities – and our racial group identity in particular. For white people, this means first struggling with what it means to be white' (p. 14).

Kovel (1988) states at the very start of his book on white racism

> that racism, far from being the simple delusion of a bigoted and ignorant minority, is a set of beliefs whose structure arises from the deepest levels of our lives – from the fabric of assumptions we make about the world, ourselves, and others, and from the patterns of our fundamental social activities. A program of action adequate to redress the wrongs of racism and to restore a just order to our society will have to encompass a substantially more radical change than that envisioned currently.
>
> (pp. 3–4)

Kovel later says:

> Racism, which diminishes its object to non-human status, also diminishes its perpetrator: all are losers by its terms. It does so, in the final analysis, by diminishing life, by reducing it to an abstraction, the better to manage it

historically. And racism thereby becomes part of the wider problem of man's compact with the natural world in which he finds himself.

(p. 233)

A hopeful endeavour

Earlier I suggested that Sam Kimbles's (2000, 2014) formulation of cultural complexes and phantom narratives offered helpful ways of linking personal and collective human dynamics. In his 2014 work, Kimbles states.

> Like all complexes . . . cultural complexes are susceptible to insight. Psychological work, whether done individually or by the collective, may transform what had been experienced as pure fact into thoughts, feelings, and beliefs that can be reflected on and altered. Individual awareness that some of one's complexes are cultural, symbolic processes derived from the group and operating at the collective level allows for the creation of a narrating third, a space for symbolization and the possibility of reflection.
>
> (p. 64)

The racist system and the privilege it brings is fully evident to black people in our societies and peculiarly invisible to whites. This restricted vision, this deafness on our part, is far more than a naive innocence but a complicit contract within the social system of conscious and unconscious power relations. In Chapter 7 I referred to W.E.B. Du Bois's realisation that the verb 'to ignore' lies at the heart of the word 'ignorance' (in Sullivan, 2006). This is no passive innocence but active complicity to maintain the status quo. If we are to confront this, we have to give up our helpless bystander role and actively challenge the perverse pact which binds us all.

In the Introduction I referred to 'the liberal commitment to justice and fairness, its dis-ease with its privileged position and the genuine wish for change'. For the most part the book since then has been about the flaws and failings of whiteness and is not a cheery read. But the liberal position is rooted in concern for other, compassion and a commitment to justice. These are the qualities that keep us looking, keep us reading, keep us acting to bring about the radical change that is required. This commitment is not altruism; it is based in an understanding that we all suffer from this system, that this privilege also damages and corrupts the souls of we white folk.

I recall seeing a poster once, many years ago, that depicted a white man carried on the back of a black man who was weighed down with his burden. The text gave the white man's words which went something like: 'I will care for you, empathise with you, weep for you for the load you have to carry. One thing I won't do is get off your back'. There is no doubt that the greater suffering is shouldered by the black man along with his burden, but the picture is not a healthy one for either. We white people need to get down, stand on our own two feet and walk – for the sake of justice, but also for our own health, our own individuation, our own peace of mind.

References

Boyd, H. (1991) *African History for Beginners*. New York: Writers and Readers Publishing Inc.

DiAngelo, R. (2018) *White Fragility. Why It's So Hard for White People to Talk About Racism*. New York: Beacon Press.

Harris, A. (2012) The House of Difference, or White Silence. *Studies in Gender and Sexuality*, 13(3), 197–216.

Harris, A. (2019) The Perverse Pact: Racism and White Privilege. *American Imago*, 76(3), 309–333

Kimbles, S. (2000) The Cultural Complex and the Myth of Invisibility. *The Vision Thing, Myth, Politics and Psyche in the World*. London: Routledge.

Kimbles, S. (2014) *Phantom Narratives: The Unseen Contributions of Culture to Psyche*. Lanham, MD: Rowman & Littlefield.

Kovel, J. (1988) *White Racism. A Psychohistory*. London: Free Association Books.

Malik, N. (2020) It Seems That Black Lives Don't Quite Matter So Much, Now That We've Got to the Hard Bit. *The Guardian Newspaper*, 06.07.2020.

McIntosh, P. (1989) White Privilege: Unpacking the Invisible Knapsack. *Peace and Freedom Magazine*, July/August, 10–12.

Sharpe, C. (2016) *In the Wake. On Blackness and Being*. Durham, NC: Duke University Press.

Sullivan, S. (2006) *Revealing Whiteness. The Unconscious Habits of Racial Privilege*. Bloomington, IN: Indiana University Press.

Walvin, J. (2007) *A Short History of Slavery*. London: Penguin.

Bibliography

Abraham, N., and Torok, M. (1994) *The Shell and the Kernel*. Vol. 1. Chicago and London: The University of Chicago Press.

Achebe, C. (1988) *Hopes and Impediments. Selected Essays 1965–87*. Suffolk: Heinemann International.

Adams, M.V. (1996) *The Multi-cultural Imagination: 'Race', Colour and the Unconscious*. London: Routledge.

Alcoff, L.M. (2015) *The Future of Whiteness*. Cambridge: Polity Press.

Altman, N. (2006) Whiteness. *Psychoanalytic Quarterly*, 75(1), 45–72.

Altman, N. (2010) *The Analyst in the Inner City. Race, Class and Culture Through a Psychoanalytic Lens*. Sussex and New York. Routledge.

Andrews, K. (2016) The Psychosis of Whiteness: The Celluloid Hallucinations of Amazing Grace and Belle. *Journal of Black Studies*, 47(5), 435–453.

Baldwin, J. (1998) The White Man's Guilt. *Collected Essays*. Ed: Orison, T. New York: Library Classics (Original work published 1965).

Bhabha, H.K. (1983) Difference, Discrimination and the Discourse of Colonialism. *The Politics of Theory*. Eds: Barker, F., Hulme, P., Iversen, D., and Loxley, D. Colchester: University of Essex Colchester Campus.

Bhabha, H.K. (1994) *The Location of Culture*. Oxon: Routledge.

Bion, W.R. (1961/1983) *Experiences in Groups*. London: Tavistock Publications.

Bion, W.R. (1962) *Learning from Experience*. London: William Heinmann Medical Books. Reprinted by Karnac Books (1984).

Bion, W.R. (1991) *A Memoir of the Future*. London: Karnacs.

Bion Talamo, P., Borgogno, F., and Merciai, S. (2000) *W.R. Bion: Between Past and Future*. London: Karnac.

Bollas, C. (1987) *The Shadow of the Object. Psychoanalysis of the Unthought Known*. London: Free Association Books.

Boyd, H. (1991) *African History for Beginners*. New York: Writers and Readers Publishing Inc.

Brand, D. (2001) *Map to the Door of No Return, Notes to Belonging*. Toronto: Vintage Canada.

Brewster, F. (2013) Wheel of Fire: The African American Dreamer and Cultural Unconsciousness. *Jung Journal: Culture and Psyche*, 7(1), 70–87.

Brewster, F. (2017) *African Americans and Jungian Psychology: Leaving the Shadows*. London: Routledge.

Brewster, F. (2019) *Archetypal Grief. Slavery's Legacy of Intergenerational Child Loss*. London and New York: Routledge, Taylor & Francis.

Brewster, F. (2020) *The Racial Complex. A Jungian Perspective on Culture and Race.* Oxon and New York: Routledge.

Brickman, C. (2018) *Race in Psychoanalysis. Aboriginal Populations in the Mind.* Oxon and New York: Routledge.

Chomsky, N. (1968) *Language and Mind.* New York: Harcourt, Brace, and World.

Ciclitira, K., and Foster, N. (2012) Attention to Culture and Diversity in Psychoanalytic Trainings. *British Journal of Psychotherapy*, 28(3), 353–373.

Coates, T. (2015) *Between the World and Me.* Melbourne: The Text Publishing Company.

Colman, W. (2016) *Act and Image. The Emergence of Symbolic Imagination.* New Orleans, LA: Spring Journal Inc.

Cooper, A. (1989) Getting Started: Psychodynamics, Racism and Anti-racism. *Journal of Social Work Practice*, 3(4), 15–27.

Cooper, A. (2010) Institutional Racism: Can Psychotherapy Change? *British Journal of Psychotherapy*, 26(4), 486–501.

Cooper, A. (2018) Institutional Racism: Can Our Organizations Change? *Conjunctions. Social Work, Psychoanalysis and Society.* Oxon: Routledge.

Cooper, A., and Lousada, J. (2005) *Borderline Welfare. Feeling and Fear of Feeling in Modern Welfare.* London: H. Karnac (Books) Ltd.

Cooper, A., and Lousada, J. (2010) The Shock of the Real: Psychoanalysis, Modernity, Survival. *Off the Couch: Contemporary Psychoanalytic Applications.* Eds: Lemma, A., and Patrick, M. London: Taylor & Francis.

Cushman, P. (2000) White Guilt, Political Activity, and the Analyst: Commentary on Paper by Neil Altman. *Psychoanalytic Dialogues*, 10(4), 607–618.

Dalal, F. (1988) Jung: A Racist. *British Journal of Psychotherapy*, 4(3), 263–279.

Dalal, F. (1998) *Taking the Group Seriously: Towards a Post-Foulkesian Group Analytic Theory.* London: Jessica Kingsley.

Dalal, F. (2001) Insides and Outsides: A Review of Psychoanalytic Renderings of Difference, Racism and Prejudice. *Psychoanalytic Studies*, 3(1), 43–66.

Dalal, F. (2002) *Race, Colour and the Process of Racialization: New Perspectives from Group Analysis, Psychoanalysis and Sociology.* Hove, East Sussex: Brunner Routledge.

Davids, F. (1998) *The Lionel Monteith Lecture, Lincoln Centre & Clinic for Psychotherapy*, Unpublished.

Davids, F. (2011) *Internal Racism: A Psychoanalytic Approach to Race and Difference.* Basingstoke: Palgrave Macmillan.

Davids, F. (2013) Why So White? *New Associations.* London: British Psychoanalytic Council.

DiAngelo, R. (2011) White Fragility. *International Journal of Critical Pedagogy*, 3(3), 54–70.

DiAngelo, R. (2018) *White Fragility. Why It's So Hard for White People to Talk About Racism.* New York: Beacon Press.

Du Bois, W.E.B. (2007) *Dusk of Dawn.* Oxford: Oxford University Press (First published in 1940 by Harcourt, Brace and World Inc.).

Du Bois, W.E.B. (2016) The Souls of White Folk. *Darkwater. Voices from Within the Veil.* London: Verso (First published in 1920 by Harcourt, Brace and Company).

Eddo-Lodge, R. (2017) *Why I'm No Longer Talking to White People About Race.* London: Bloomsbury Circus.

Ellis, E. (2013) Silenced: The Black Student Experience. *Therapy Today*, December. www.therapytoday.net

Evans Holmes, D. (1992) Race and Transference in Psychoanalysis and Psychotherapy. *International Journal of Psychoanalysis*, 73(1), 1–11.

Fanon, F. (1986) *Black Skin, White Masks*. London: Pluto Press (First published in 1952 by Editions de Seuil).

Fanon, F. (1990) *The Wretched of the Earth*. London: Penguin Books (First published in 1965 by Macgibbon & Kee).

Fletchman Smith, B. (2000) *Mental Slavery. Psychoanalytic Studies of Caribbean People*. London: Rebus Press.

Fletchman Smith, B. (2011) *Transcending the Legacies of Slavery. A Psychoanalytic View*. London: Karnac Books.

Folha, de S. Paulo (1998) *Racismo Cordial*, Second Edn. Sao Paulo: Ática.

Freud, S. (1913) Totem and Taboo: Some Points of Agreement Between the Mental Lives of Savages and Neurotics. *The Origin of Religion: Totem and Taboo, Moses and Monotheism and Other Works*. Vol 13. London: Penguin.

Frosh, S. (1989) Psychoanalysis and Racism. *Crisis of the Self: Further Essays on Psychoanalysis and Politics*. Ed: Richards, B. London: Free Association Books.

Frosh, S. (2013) *Hauntings: Psychoanalysis and Ghostly Transmissions*. London: Palgrave Macmillan.

Frosh, S. (2017) Primitivity and Violence: Traces of the Unconscious in Psychoanalysis. *Journal of Theoretical and Philosophical Psychology*, 37(1), 34–47.

Frosh, S., and Baraitser, L. (2008) Psychoanalysis and Psychosocial Studies. *Psychoanalysis, Culture & Society*, 13, 346–365.

Gilman, S. (1993) *Freud, Race and Gender*. Princeton, NJ: Princeton University Press.

Gordon, P. (1993). Keeping Therapy White?: Psychotherapy Trainings and Equal Opportunities. *British Journal of Psychotherapy*, 10(1), 44–49.

Gordon, P. (1993). Souls in Armour: Thoughts on Psychoanalysis and Racism. *British Journal of Psychotherapy*, 10(1), 62–76.

Green, A. (1970) The Dead Mother. *On Private Madness*. London: Hogarth Press.

Grinberg, L. (1985) *Introduction to the Work of Bion*. London: Karnac (First published in 1975 by the Roland Harris Educational Trust).

Harris, A. (2012) The House of Difference, or White Silence. *Studies in Gender and Sexuality*, 13(3), 197–216.

Harris, A. (2019) The Perverse Pact: Racism and White Privilege. *American Imago*, 76(3), 309–333.

Hartman, S. (2007) *Lose Your Mother. A Journey Along the Atlantic Slave Route*. New York: Farrar, Straus and Giroux.

Hazlewood, N. (2004) *The Queen's Slave Trader. John Hawkyns, Elizabeth I and the Trafficking in Human Souls*. London and New York: Harper Perennial.

Henderson, J.L. (1988) The Cultural Unconscious. *Quadrant: Journal of the C. G. Jung Foundation for Analytical Psychology*, 21(2), 7–16.

Henderson, J. (1990) The Cultural Unconscious. In *Shadow and Self*. Wilmette, IL: Chiron Publications.

Henry, W. (2007) *Whiteness Made Simple. Stepping into the Grey Zone*. London: Nu-Beyond Ltd.

Hillman, J. (1986) Notes on White Supremacy. Essaying an Archetypal Account of Historical Events. *Spring Publications*, 29–58.

Hirschfeld, L.A. (2012) Seven Myths of Race and the Young Child. *Du Bois Review*, 9(1), 17–39.

Hogenson, G. (2004) Emergence and the Psyche's Deep Structure. *Analytical Psychology: Contemporary Perspectives in Jungian Analysis*. Hove, East Sussex: Brunner Routledge.

Hoggett, P. (1992) The Art of the Possible. *Partisans in an Uncertain World: The Psychoanalysis of Engagement*. London: Free Association Books.

Hoggett, P. (2008) What's in a Hyphen? Reconstructing Psychosocial Studies. *Psychoanalysis, Culture & Society*, 13, 379–384.

James-Franklin, M. (2004) *Processes of Adaptation in Black Trainee Therapists*, Unpublished Dissertation, MSc in the Psychodynamics of Human Development, Birkbeck College, University of London.

Jung, C.G. (1921) The Type Problem in Poetry. *Psychological Types*. The Collected Works of C. G. Jung. Vol. 6. London and Princeton, NJ: Routledge & Kegan Paul/Princeton University Press.

Jung, C.G. (1928/1966) The Relations Between the Ego and the Unconscious. *Two Essays on Analytical Psychology*. Collected Works 7. Princeton, NJ: Princeton University Press.

Jung, C.G. (1935) *The Symbolic Life*. Collected Works 18. Princeton, NJ: Princeton University Press.

Jung, C.G. (1938) Psychological Aspects of the Mother Archetype. *The Archetypes and the Collective Unconscious*. Collected Works 9i. Princeton, NJ: Princeton University Press.

Jung, C.W. (1939) The Dreamlike World of India. *Civilization in Transition*. Collected Works 10. Princeton, NJ: Princeton University Press.

Jung, C.G. (1948) Healing the Split. *The Symbolic Life*. Collected Works 18. Princeton, NJ: Princeton University Press.

Jung, C.G. (1963) *Memories, Dreams and Reflections*. New York: Pantheon.

Kaufmann, M. (2017) *Black Tudors. The Untold Story*. London: Oneworld.

Keval, N. (2016) *Racist States of Mind. Understanding the Perversion of Curiosity and Concern*. London: Karnac Books Ltd.

Kimbles, S. (2000) The Cultural Complex and the Myth of Invisibility. *The Vision Thing, Myth, Politics and Psyche in the World*. London: Routledge.

Kimbles, S. (2014) *Phantom Narratives: The Unseen Contributions of Culture to Psyche*. Lanham, MD: Rowman & Littlefield.

Knox, J. (2003) *Archetype, Attachment, Analysis. Jungian Psychology and the Emergent Mind*. Hove, East Sussex: Brunner-Routledge.

Kovel, J. (1988) *White Racism. A Psychohistory*. London: Free Association Books.

Kovel, J. (2000) Reflections on White Racism. *Psychoanalytic Dialogues*, 10(4), 579–587.

Lacan, J. (1987) *The Four Fundamental Concepts of Psycho-analysis*. London: Peregrine Books.

Lane, C. (1998) The Psychoanalysis of Race: An Introduction. *The Psychoanalysis of Race*. Ed: Lane, C. New York: Columbia University Press.

Lousada, J. (1997) The Hidden History of an Idea: The Difficulties of Adopting Anti-racism. *Integrity and Change, Mental Health in the Market Place*. Ed: Smith, E. London: Routledge.

Lowe, F. (2006) Racism as a Borderline Issue: The Avoidance and Marginalization of Race in Psychotherapy. *Difference: An Avoided Topic in Practice*. Eds: Foster et al. London: Karnac.

Lowe, F. (Ed.) (2014) *Thinking Space. Promoting Thinking About Race, Culture, and Diversity in Psychotherapy and Beyond.* Tavistock Clinic Series. London: Karnac.

Macpherson, W. (1999) *The Stephen Lawrence Inquiry: Report of an Inquiry*. London: HM Stationery Office.

Mills, C. (1997) *The Racial Contract*. Ithaca, NY: Cornell University Press.

Mills, C. (2007) White Ignorance. *Race and Epistemologies of Ignorance*. Eds: Sullivan, S., and Tuana, T. Albany, NY: State University of New York Press.

Mitchell, S.A. (2000) You've Got to Suffer If You Want to Sing the Blues: Psychoanalytic Reflections on Guilt and Self-Pity. *Psychoanalytic Dialogues*, 10(5), 713–733.

Morgan, H. (2000) Modern Western Society. The Making of Myth and Meaning. *Jungian Thought in the Modern World*. Eds: Christopher, E., and McFarland Solomon, H. London: Free Association Books.

Morgan, H. (2002) Exploring Racism. *Journal of Analytical Psychology*, 47(4), 567–581.

Morgan, H. (2007) The Effects of Difference of 'Race' and Colour in Supervision. *On Supervision. Psychoanalytic and Jungian Analytic Perspectives*. Eds. Petts, A., and Shapley, B. London: Karnac.

Morgan, H. (2008) Issues of 'Race' in Psychoanalytic Psychotherapy: Whose Problem Is It Anyway? *British Journal of Psychotherapy*, 24(1), 34–49.

Morgan, H. (2014) Between Fear and Blindness – The White Therapist and the Black Patient. *Thinking Space*. Ed: Lowe, F. London: Karnac.

Morgan, H. (2019) Response to Fanny Brewster and Alan Vaughan. *Journal of Analytical Psychology*, 64(3), 349–366.

Morrison, T. (2007) *Beloved*. London: Vintage (First published 1987).

Novick, K. (2018) Learning the Difference Between Hate and Violence. *Before and After Violence. Developmental, Clinical and Sociocultural Aspects*. Ed: Akhtar, S. London: Lexington Books.

Parker, R.N. (2019) Slavery in the White Psyche. *Psychoanalytic Social Work*, 26, 1.

Plasa, C. (2000) *Textual Politics from Slavery to Postcolonialism. Race and Identification*. Basingstoke: Palgrave Macmillan.

Radin, P. (1927). *Primitive Man as Philosopher*. Reprinted by New York Review of Books Classics (2017). Oxford: Blackwell.

Rankin, C. (2020) *Just Us. An American Conversation*. London: Allen Lane.

Rosenfeld, H. (1971) A Clinical Approach to the Psychoanalytic Theory of the Life and Death Instincts: An Investigation into the Aggressive Aspects of Narcissism. *International Journal of Psychoanalysis*, 52, 169–178.

Rustin, M. (1991) Psychoanalysis, Racism and Anti-racism. *The Good Society and the Inner World*. London: Verso.

Samuels, A. (1985) *Jung and the Post-Jungians*. London, Boston, and Henley: Routledge & Kegan Paul.

Samuels, A. (2018) Jung and 'Africans': A Critical and Contemporary Review of Some of the Issues. *International Journal of Jungian Studies*, 10, 2.

Schwab, G. (2010) *Haunting Legacies; Violent Histories and Transgenerational Trauma*. New York: Columbia University Press.

Sharpe, C. (2016) *In the Wake. On Blackness and Being*. Durham, NC: Duke University Press.

Singer, T., and Kaplinsky, C. (2010) Cultural Complexes in Analysis. *Jungian Psychoanalysis: Working in the Spirit of C.G. Jung*. Ed: Stein, M. Chicago: Open Court.

Singer, T., and Kimbles, S. (2004) *The Cultural Complex: Contemporary Jungian Perspectives on Psyche and Society*. Hove, East Sussex: Routledge.

Singer, T., and Kimbles, S. (2004) The Emerging Theory of Cultural Complexes. *Analytical Psychology. Contemporary Perspectives in Jungian Analysis*. Eds: Cambray, J., and Carte, L. Hove, East Sussex and New York: Routledge.

Smith, L. (1994) *Killers of the Dream.* New York: Norton & Company Inc.

Stein, R. (2005) Why Perversion? 'False Love' and the Perverse Pact. *International Journal of Psychoanalysis*, 86(3), 775–799.

Straker, G. (2004) Race for Cover: Castrated Whiteness, Perverse Consequences. *Psychoanalytic Dialogues*, 14(4), 405–422.

Suchet, M. (2007) Unravelling Whiteness. *Psychoanalytic Dialogues*, 17(6), 867–886.

Sullivan, S. (2006) *Revealing Whiteness. The Unconscious Habits of Racial Privilege.* Bloomington, IN: Indiana University Press.

Sullivan, S. (2014) *Good White People. The Problem With Middle-Class Anti-racism.* Albany: State University of NY Press.

Symington, J., & Symington, N. (1996) *The Clinical Thinking of Wilfred Bion.* London: Routledge.

Taylor, H. (2013) *UK Psychoanalysis*: *Mistaking the Part for the Whole.* British Psychoanalytic Council Discussion Paper.

Thomas, L. (1992) Racism and Psychotherapy: Working with Racism in the Consulting Room – An Analytic View. *Intercultural Therapy.* Eds: Kareem, J., and Littlewood, R. Oxford: Blackwood Scientific Publications.

Tolleson, J. (2009) Saving the World One Patient at a Time: Psychoanalysis and Social Critique. *Psychotherapy and Politics International*, 7(3), 190–205.

Troyna, B., and Hatcher, R. (1992) *Racism in Children's Lives: A Study of Mainly White Primary Schools.* New York: Routledge.

UK Equalities and Human Rights Commission (2016) *Healing a Divided Britain: The Need for a Comprehensive Race Equality Strategy.* London: Equality and Human Rights Commission.

Unsworth, B. (1988) *Sugar and Rum.* New York: Norton and Company.

Unsworth, B. (1992) *Sacred Hunger.* London: Penguin Books.

Unsworth, B. (2012) *The Quality of Mercy.* London: Windmill Books.

Van Ausdale, D., and Feagin, J. (2001) *The First R: How Children Learn Race and Racism.* Lanham, MD: Rowman & Littlefield.

Vaughan, A. (2019) African American Cultural History and Reflection on Jung in the African Diaspora. *Journal of Analytical Psychology*, 64(3), 320–348.

Walvin, J. (2007) *A Short History of Slavery.* London: Penguin.

Winnicott, D.W. (1974) *Playing and Reality.* London: Penguin.

Wolfenstein, E.V. (1989) *The Victims of Democracy. Malcolm X and the Black Revolution.* London: Free Association Books.

Young, R. (1994) Psychoanalysis and Racism: A Loud Silence. *Mental Space.* London: Process Press.

Index

Abolition of the Slave Trade Act 38
Abraham, Nicolas 29, 33, 36
Adams, Michael Vannoy 77, 82
Adams, Tim 38
African Americans xii–xiii, 23, 80, 83,
  89–90; analytical psychology and
  77–78; laws and 2; legacy of slavery 30,
  32; longitudinal study of 61
African Holocaust 25, 90; see also slavery;
  transatlantic slave trade
Agbetu, Toyin 40
Alcoff, Linda 13, 14, 21, 88
Allen, Theodore 14
all lives matter 86, 87
Altman, Neil 109–110
Amazing Grace (film) 39
Analyst in the Inner City, The (Altman)
  110
Apted, Michael 39
Aquinas, Thomas 27
archetype 76, 80–81; concept of 81;
  cultural unconscious 82, 89; structures
  79–81
Aristotle 27
Arne, Thomas 40
Asante, Amma 39

badness 10, 15, 58
Baldwin, James 116
BAME *see* Black, Asian and Minority
  Ethnic (BAME) communities
Baraitser, Lisa 112, 113
Belle (film) 39
Beloved (Morrison) 31
Bennett, Liza 25
Bhabha, Homi 80, 91
biological essentialism 45
Bion, W.R. 23–24, 90–91, 113

black 12, 92; category 64; disparagement
  of 50; division of white and 37; label
  15; polarity 14; term 1–2, 13, 127–128;
  white and 14
Black and Asian Therapy Network
  (BAATN) 105
Black, Asian and Minority Ethnic (BAME)
  communities xii, 1, 8, 102; experience
  of trainees 103–108
Black Lives Matter (BLM) ix, xii, 40,
  85–87, 130–131
blackness 1, 12, 15, 93–94; disparagement
  of 50, 125; notion of 18; putting aside
  114–115; slavery and 27; value of 54
black 'Other' xiii, 54, 67, 126
Black Skin, White Masks (Fanon) 53
Black Tudors (Kaufmann) 27
'blanche' 67
BLM *see* Black Lives Matter (BLM)
Boas, Franz 73
Boechat, Paula 108
Boechat, Walter 108
Borderline Welfare (Cooper and Lousada) 92
Brewster, Fanny xiii, 30–31, 77–78, 90, 111
Brickman, Celia 5, 28, 44, 73, 75, 82
Britain, slavery and 38–40
British Association of Psychotherapists
  (BAP) 104
British Journal of Psychotherapy
  (journal) 78
British Jungian Analytic Association
  (BJAA) 114
British Psychoanalytic Council 102, 104

Cameron, David 39
Chambers dictionary 53
Civil Rights Movement x, 1–2
clinical work, racism in consulting 48–52

collective unconscious, Jung on 78–82
Collingwood, Luke 132
Colman, Warren 74, 81
colonialism 7, 12, 36,
colour 1; centre and the margins 17–18
colour blindness: racism and 54–55;
    whiteness and 62–64
Colston, Edward ix, 133
consulting room: cuckoo in the nest 51,
    52–53; Dee in 48–52; Janet in 57–58,
    69–70; racism in 48–52; whitewash in
    51, 53–54
Cooper, Andrew 92–93, 95, 97–98, 106, 107
cordial racism 108–109
counter-transference 49, 51, 58, 124, 125,
    127
Covid-19 xii–xiii, 47, 85
cuckoo in the nest 51, 53–54
cultural complex 9, 89–92, 115, 135
cultural unconscious 30, 89; concept
    of 82
Cumberbatch, Benedict 25
Curry, Andrew 51
Cushman, Philip 4–5

Dalal, Farhad xi, xiii, 6–7, 17–18, 21–22,
    54, 78, 88, 106, 111, 119–121
Darwin, Charles 44
Davids, Fakhry 6–7, 93, 111, 123
dead mother, concept of 8, 67
deadness 68, 70
Dennis, Maxine 104
DiAngelo, Robin 6, 8, 10, 17, 18–21, 62,
    90, 108, 134
disability 10, 18, 20, 22
Du Bois, W.E.B. 89, 102–103, 135
dynamic repression, Freud's theory of 29

Eddo-Lodge, Reno 12
Ejiofor, Chiwetel 25
Ekpenyon, Oku 40
Elias, Norbert 6
Elizabeth (Queen) 27
Ellis, Eugene 105, 107, 109
Empire Pays Back, The (documentary) 36
Encyclopaedia Britannica 52
Eng, David 37
Equiano, Olaudah 39
essentialism 45, 106
European Enlightenment 39, 72
European Holocaust 29
Evans Holmes, Dorothy 124
exceptionalism 10, 90, 102

Fanon, Frantz 53, 76, 79, 93, 111
fantasy fetish 91
Fletchman Smith, Barbara 32–33
Floyd, George xii, 86, 97, 99, 130–131,
    133
Foulkes, S.H. 6
Freud, Sigmund 8, 73, 74, 75, 80, 109;
    'civilised' and 'primitive' 72; 'primitive'
    72–73; social thought 75; Totem and
    Taboo 73; unconscious 72
Frosh, Stephen 29, 74, 109, 112, 113

Garner, Margaret 31
gender 22; identity 17–18; injustice 10,
    102, 114; problem of bias 80
Goldberg, Arnold 69, 125
Gone With the Wind (film) 34
goodness 15, 59–60, 97, 103, 126
Green, Andre 8, 67–68, 109, 121
Guardian (newspaper) 28, 40, 131
guilt: concept of 8; emotion 19, 21, 91,
    108; healthy 96; racism 22; shame and
    36–37, 55, 58–60, 115, 119, 123
guiltiness 58–60; concept of 8; notion of
    96; remorse and 70; term 60
'guilty whiteness' 60

Haeckel, Ernst 44–45, 72–73
Han, Shinhee 37
Harris, Adrienne 8, 60, 67, 87, 91, 99, 109,
    111, 121, 130–131, 134
Hartman, Saidya 25
Hartman, Stephen 23–24
Hawkyns, John 27
Henderson, Joseph 82, 89
Henry VII (King) 28
Heschel, Abraham Joshua (Rabbi) 130
Hillman, James 12, 15, 20, 72, 82
Hirsch, Afua 40
Hirschfeld, Lawrence 63–64
Hoggett, Paul 9, 112
Holocaust 29, 33, 37; African 25, 90
Human Genome Project 1, 7, 45

ignorance 8, 87, 103, 106, 135; BLM
    and 87; colour blindness and white 8,
    20–22; depth of 79; Du Bois on 135; of
    innocence 21; knowing about 23; racism
    and ix; white 23, 23–24, 103
Igwe, Angus 120
imaginary whiteness 14–15
individualism xiii, 10, 14, 88
individuation, model of xiii

institutional racism: definition 106;
tackling 107
Internal Racism (Davids) 6
In the Wake (Sharpe) 9, 132
Invention of the White Race, Vol 1, The
(Allen) 14
Islamophobia 128
Ixion 77, 78

James I (King) 28
James, William 89
James-Franklin, Margaret 103
Jim Crow laws 2–3
Jung, C.G. xi, 8, 73, 74, 80; becoming
'civilised' 76–78; collective unconscious
78–82, 88; decolonising the theory
82–83; 'primitive' 72–73
Jungian analysis/Jungian analytic
perspective 4, 109, 119

Kareem, Jafar 101
Karpman's Drama Triangle 98
Katerud, Sigmund 69
Katz, Phyllis 61, 63
Kaufmann, Miranda 27
Keval, Narendra 93, 95, 111
Kimbles, Sam 30, 82, 89–90, 98–99, 111,
115, 135
King, Martin Luther 23, 38
K link, Bion's 23–24
Knox, Jean 81
Kovel, Joel 44, 46, 111, 115, 134

Lamarck, Jean-Baptiste 44, 72
Lawrence, Stephen 106
LGBTQ community 102
Ligali 40
Linnaeus, Carolus 44
Lousada, Julian 59, 66, 92–93, 95, 98
Lowe, Frank 104, 111, 115

MacMullan, Terrance 2
Macpherson, Sir William 106
Malik, Nesrine 131
Martin, Trayvon xii, 86
McIntosh, Peggy 133
McQueen, Steve 25
Mental Slavery (Fletchman Smith) 32
Miller, Joseph 26, 34, 35
Mills, Charles 21, 23
Mitchell, Stephen 60, 96
Morrison, Toni 31
mother, term 70n2

NAFSIYAT, Intercultural Therapy Centre
101
Novick, Kerry 98

Observer (journal) 38
Oduye, Adepero 25
one-drop test 15

Parker, Ryan 34–35, 37–38, 68, 98
Partisans in an Uncertain World (Hoggett) 9
personal transference 51
perverse pact 9, 91, 97, 135; concept of 9
phantom narratives 30, 82, 90, 99, 115,
133, 135
potentiality 32
power dynamics 8, 18, 92, 121
preservative repression 29
pre-transference 51
'primitive' 37, 41, 43–45; black as 28, 43,
76–77; characteristic 79; concept of 114;
Freud and Jung 8, 41, 72–73; Jung on
xi; in psychoanalytic discourse 74–75;
state of mind 80; term 74, 75
Primitive Culture (Tyler) 44
Primitive Man as Philosopher (Radin) 79
Problem of Slavery as History, The
(Miller) 26
projection(s) 3, 4, 48, 50, 58–59, 67, 68,
80, 88, 105, 124, 125, 127
projective identification 127
Prospect (magazine) 86
'proto-mental' phenomena 90, 91
psychic crypts 30
psychic gang 95–96
psychoanalysis: animus/anima 114;
complacency in 112–113; inner and
outer 111–112; participation mystique
114; problematic history 109–111;
psychoanalytic perspective 4–7; ways
going forward 113–116
psychoanalytic psychotherapist 17, 32,
103–104, 110, 113, 118
psychoanalytic psychotherapy 75, 101,
103, 107, 112, 115
'psychose blanche' 66–69, 109; concept of
8, 67, 121; of disavowal 123
psychotherapy: assessment of supervision
127–128; black therapist and white
patient 125–127; black therapists on
racism in 119; race and racism in
101–103; supervision in 118–121;
whiteness in 128–129; white therapist and
black patient 122–125; *see also* therapy

Quality of Mercy, The (Unsworth) 36

race 1; centre and the margins 17–18; concept of 37; death rate and Covid-19 pandemic 47; modern developments 45–46; origins of 43–45; racism today 46–48
Race in Psychoanalysis (Brickman) 75
racial complex 85–88, 98–99; black bystanders 94; Black Lives Matter 85–87; boy 93–94; Brewster's 90; cultural complex 89–92; doctor 96–97; doctor's surgery 92–93; mother 94; social unconscious 88–89; white bystanders 97–98; woman 94–96
Racial Contract, The (Mills) 21
racism 1; colour blindness 62–64; in consulting room 48–52; cordial 108–109; cuckoo in the nest 51, 52–53; disavowal of whiteness 121–122; discussion in psychotherapy 101–103; institutional 106, 107; psychic geography of 93; psychoanalytic perspective 4–7; today 46–48; wake and 132–135; white 2, 46, 134; whitewash and 49–50, 51, 53–54
'Racismo Cordial' 108
Radin, Paul 73, 79
Refugee Therapy Centre 101
relational psychoanalysis 111

Samuels, Andrew xiii, 73, 78–79
savage 43, 45, 73, 76, 114
Schwab, Gabriele 31, 33, 37
sexuality 22; identity 17–18; infantile 72; injustice 10, 102, 114; problem of bias 80; projection of 58
shadow(s) xii, xiii, 10, 15, 50, 58, 77, 82, 95, 124, 125
Shahvisi, Arianne 86, 87
Shamdasani, Sonu 73
shame: concept of 8; guilt and 36–37, 55, 58–60, 115, 119, 123
Sharpe, Christina 9, 132
Shell and the Kernel, The (Abraham and Torok) 29
Singer, Tom 82, 89–90
slavery: Bible story and 130–131; black people today and 132–133; Britain and 38–40; Europe and slave trade 35–36, 72; Europe before transatlantic slave trade 26–27; history in United States 78; legacy for descendants of enslaved

Africans 31–33; legacy for perpetrators 33–35; legacy of 25–26; mourning and melancholia 36–41; ship from Africa to Americas 132; transatlantic 27–29; *see also* transatlantic slave trade
social identity, aspects of 13
social unconscious 6, 9, 88–89, 98
solipsism, white 3, 8, 16, 20, 67, 90
splits/splitting 4, 48, 58, 59, 66, 67, 69, 88, 124; horizontal 66; vertical xii, 8, 66–69, 109, 121, 125
Stalinism 29
St Augustine 27
Stein, Ruth 91
Stevenson, Bryan 38
subjective whiteness 16
Suchet, Melanie 17, 37, 111
Sullivan, Shannon 2–3, 16, 102
supervision 118–121; assessment 127–128; whiteness and 128–129

Taylor, Breonna xii, 86
Taylor, Harvey 110
Tay-Sachs disease 45
therapy: black therapist and white patient 125–127; cuckoo in the nest 51, 52–53; Dee example 48–52; Janet example 57–58, 69–70; racism in the consulting room 48–52; white therapist and black patient 122–125; whitewash and 49–50, 51, 53–54; *see also* psychotherapy
Thomas, Lennox 50–51, 101, 123–124
Thomson, James 40
Tolleson, Jennifer 110
Torok, Maria 29, 33, 36
Totem and Taboo (Freud) 73
transatlantic slave trade 27–29; Europe before 26–27; legacy of 25–26; transgenerational trauma 29–31; *see also* slavery
Transcending the Legacies of Slavery (Fletchman Smith) 32
transference 7, 49, 51, 55, 57, 66, 69, 83, 118, 123, 124, 126
transgenerational transmission of trauma 7, 29–31
Twelve Years a Slave (film) 25–26
Tyler, E.B. 44

UK Equalities and Human Rights Commission 46
unconscious habits 16, 89
University of Colorado 61

Vaughan, Alan 81–82, 83

waiting room incident: black bystanders 94; *Borderline Welfare* 92; boy in 93–94; doctor in 96–97; doctor's surgery in 92–93; mother in 94; white bystanders 97–98; woman in 94–96
Walvin, James 27, 132
white 92; black and 14; category 64; definition of 12; division of black and 37; label 15; polarity 14, privilege 16–17; supremacy 2–3, 12, 15, 34, 53, 72; term 13
white fragility: concept of 8; DiAngelo on 10, 18–20, 21, 90, 108, 134
White Fragility (DiAngelo) 108
white ignorance, Bion's 'minus K' 23–24
white liberal 3, 13, 37, 47–48, 59, 61–62, 67, 74, 98, 109, 121, 126
white mask, definition 53–54
whiteness 1; colour blindness 62–64; colour blindness and white ignorance 20–22; concept of 12; disavowal of 65–66, 121–122; empirical 14; imaginary 14–15; learning 61–62; 'psychose blanche' 66–69; psychosis of 39; psychotherapy and 128–129;

shame, guilt and 'guiltiness' 58–60; subjective 16; work of 7–9; work of dismantling 131
white privilege 16–17, 54, 113; concept of 8, 10; disavowal of 60, 66, 98, 109, 121; modern-day 38; promoting 88; protecting 21, 90; racism and 59, 67, 87, 91; unconscious habits of 16; white fragility and 108; white supremacy and 2–3
white racism 2, 134
White Racism (Kovel) 46, 134
white supremacy 2–3, 12, 15, 34, 53, 72
'white tribe' 23, 24
whitewash 53–54
Why I'm No Longer Talking to White People About Race (Eddo-Lodge) 12
Wilberforce, William 38–39
Windrush generation ix–x
Winnicott, D.W. 68
Word Association Test 89
Working with Racism in the Consulting Room (Thomas) 50

Young, Bob 103

Zimmerman, George xii, 86

9 780367 218362